Important Bird Areas *of* Nevada

D. E. McIvor

Lahontan Audubon Society
Reno, Nevada

Important Bird Areas of Nevada
by Donald E. McIvor

Copyright 2005 by the Lahontan Audubon Society
P.O. Box 2304
Reno, NV 89505
All rights reserved. Published 2005.
http://www.NevadaAudubon.org

Book design, cover design, and layout by D. E. McIvor
Set in Garamond and Gil Sans MT
Printed at Reno Printing

Printing generously funded by the Rio Tinto – BirdLife International
Programme/Rio Tinto Partnership Action Fund and by the U.S. Fish and
Wildlife Service - Nevada Fish and Wildlife Office.

Front cover illustration © Ray Nelson 2005. http://www.raynelsonart.com.
        The unlikely congregation of birds depicted on the cover are all
        species of concern in Nevada. These birds and many others
        face an uncertain future due to degradation, fragmentation, and
        outright loss of the sagebrush-steppe. Each bird–Ferruginous
        Hawk, Prairie Falcon, Greater Sage-Grouse, Sage Thrasher,
        Sage Sparrow, and Burrowing Owl–is staring into the eyes of
        the viewer as a challenge to do all that we can to preserve
        remaining essential habitat to ensure their survival.

Back cover photograph Carson Lake (Lahontan Valley IBA) and Stillwater
Range. All photographs in the book are © D. E. McIvor/Hinterlands unless
otherwise credited.

Frontispiece: Nevada's Important Bird Areas.

ISBN 13:   978-0-9703438-2-6
ISBN 10:   0-9703438-2-5

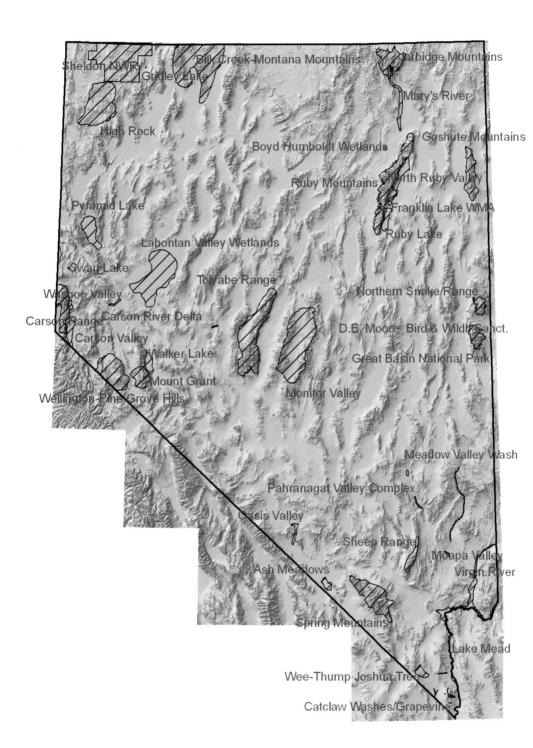

This is the singular magic of birds–to exist on two planes, as biological entities of bones and tissue, but also to live a separate existence in the human heart, and in both respects–physical and metaphysical–tying up the scattered and beleaguered wild places of the world and knitting them into a seamless whole by the simple act of flight.

–Scott Weidensaul

Table of Contents

Acknowledgments

An undertaking of this sort cannot be successful without the labor of many people. When a nonprofit organization spearheads an effort like this, it is with the understanding that the program will rely heavily on the generosity of many people, agencies, and organizations to donate time and effort. And so it is that as this milestone comes to pass I am casting back to recall all those who have contributed to this effort. Inevitably, someone who deserves recognition will be overlooked, but please know that every contribution is still appreciated the Lahontan Audubon Society and I extend our sincerest thanks.

Support and enthusiasm for the Important Bird Areas (IBA) Program in Nevada started with Graham Chisholm, Jim Eidel, and Dave Straley. Grant writing and hiring efforts were assisted by Ted Floyd and Alan Gubanich. For their various efforts to initiate the program I am grateful.

The Lahontan Audubon Society's past and present Board of Directors and Trustees continue to support the Nevada IBA Program. This is an over-worked group of volunteers who deserves everyone's thanks for their efforts on behalf of all of Nevada's wildlife. Taking on their first paid employee and initiating this program was a courageous step towards developing a comprehensive conservation program. I have had many informative discussions with various Board members that helped fashion the program's direction. I am particularly grateful to Dave Straley–every organization can only hope to have a treasurer (and past president) as competent. I am grateful to Nancy Bish, Ray Nelson, and especially Ali Chaney for their input into the program. It is an honor to have Ray's art gracing this book's cover.

The Nevada IBA Program is a partnership with the National IBA Program administered by the National Audubon Society. I would like to thank Dan Niven and John Cecil for their oversight and input over the years and their relentless work to see this program succeed on a national level. Several state IBA coordinators have also provided great insights along the way, particularly Dan Cooper, Steve Hoffman, and Patrick Comins.

The Nevada IBA Program relied on a Technical Advisory Committee (TAC) to review site nominations. From the start I viewed this group as dynamic, with members contributing what time they could before work or personal obligations drew them elsewhere. TAC members who helped develop Nevada's IBA criteria and review sites include Nancy Bish, Doug Booth, Pete Bradley, Peter Brussard, Erick Campbell, Dorothy Crowe, Jim Eidel, Mary Jo Elpers, Ted Floyd, Kevin Kritz, Jeri Krueger, Kevin Mack, Lew Oring, Rose Strickland, John Swett, and Ken Voget.

Several individuals stepped up and took on site nominations. Most of these sites would not be in our portfolio of IBAs if not for the efforts of Styron Bell, Nancy Bish, Mike Boyles, Pete Bradley, Bill and Beth Clark, Cali Crampton, Neal Darby, Jim Eidel, Mary Jo Elpers, Bob Goodman, Bill Henry, Bruce Lund, Jeff Mackay, David Moore, Jim Moore, Jennifer Newmark, Mark and Lois

Ports, Mike San Miguel, David St. George, Melissa Renfro, Rose Strickland, Carolyn Titus, Cris Tomlinson, Ken Voget, Jack Walters, and Therese Werst. Dr. Robert Chipley was also very helpful in the early days of the Nevada IBA Program in helping to bring me up to speed on the efforts of the American Bird Conservancy in Nevada and their Important Bird Areas Program.

Dr. Scott Mensing and Professor Gary Johnson of the University of Nevada, Reno Geography Department facilitated an advanced ArcGIS class project that helped the Nevada IBA Program immensely. Three students in this class, Andy Simpson, Monte Sandford, and Jeremy McHugh, took on the IBA Program as a class project and developed the ArcGIS coverage on which I rely on almost a daily basis. The frontispiece in this book is derived from their work.

Collaborators on the IBA Program extend beyond individuals to encompass other non-governmental organizations and federal and state agencies. The Great Basin Bird Observatory and The Nature Conservancy have been most helpful. Ted Floyd permitted access to unpublished data from the Nevada Breeding Bird Atlas, which proved invaluable for informing IBA nominations. The Nevada Department of Wildlife provided both data and, from particular individuals, insight into conservation and politics in the state. I am grateful to Nevada State Parks for the conservation work we have initiated on the Carson River Delta IBA. Among federal agencies, Bureau of Reclamation, U.S. National Park Service, Bureau of Land Management, U.S. Forest Service, and the U.S. Fish and Wildlife Service all support the program and have contributed to its success.

Several individuals provided valuable reviews of early drafts of this book. These reviewers include John Cecil, Ali Chaney, Jim Eidel, Alan Gubanich, Karen Kish, and Kevin Kritz.

Finally, I wish to thank all the agencies, foundations, organizations, and corporations that have financially supported the IBA Program. Clearly, there would never have been a Nevada IBA Program without the generosity and foresight of these supporters: A. B. Schultz Foundation, Charles H. Stout Foundation, G. S. Whittell Fund, Harris Foundation, Humboldt-Toiyabe National Forest, National Audubon Society, National Fish and Wildlife Foundation, Nevada Division of State Lands, Patagonia, Inc., Rio Tinto – BirdLife International Programme/Rio Tinto Partnership Action Fund, and The Wilburforce Foundation.

Don McIvor
Carson City, Nevada
September 2005

Introduction

History of the IBA Program

The Important Bird Areas Program was conceived in the United Kingdom in the mid-1980s and grew from a need recognized by BirdLife International (then International Council of Bird Preservation) to identify areas critical to the survival of birds. BirdLife International developed a model early in the process whereby a set of criteria were established, sites nominated, and then evaluated against the criteria. Initial efforts favored wetlands, in part because the first set of criteria relied on established criteria such as those used by the Ramsar Convention for protecting wetlands (Wells 1998). According to BirdLife International (2004a), IBAs have at least one of three qualities:

- have significant numbers of one or more globally threatened species,
- are one of a set of sites that together hold a suite of restricted-range species or biome-restricted species, or
- have exceptionally large numbers of migratory or congregatory species.

To further refine the concept of IBAs, BirdLife International recognized that more criteria were needed than simply absolute numbers of birds using a site. An IBA must be amenable to conservation action and management, and each IBA should be large enough to support self-sustaining populations of the key bird species for which it was identified (BirdLife International 2004a). In the case of migrants, it should fulfill their life-history needs for the duration of the birds' use of the site. Regional partners have flexibility in adapting these broad criteria to conform to local conservation needs and to make sense in the context of the local avifauna.

One tangible result of the initial years of the program was *Important Bird Areas of Europe* (Grimmett 1989). The book identified 2,444 IBAs in 31 countries. In testimony to the validity of BirdLife International's approach and to the timeliness of the effort, the book became a blueprint for habitat protection. The second tangible result of these early efforts was a network of recognized and, in many cases, protected sites established across much of Europe. The European Community embraced the IBA concept and urged its member countries to provide special protection status to these sites. By the mid-1990s, more than 16 million acres of habitat had been give some degree of protective status as a result of their identification as IBAs. (Wells 1998)

The IBA Program has now spread to every continent including Antarctica, and as of 2005 the number of IBAs globally has exceeded 7,000 sites in nearly 170 nations (J. Cecil, National Audubon Society, pers. comm.). In 2003, BirdLife International began grappling with the unique challenges of implementing the IBA Program in the open seas, working to identify critical areas for, among others, pelagic species that roam widely and may only come to land every few years to breed.

The IBA Program arrived in the United States in 1995, with the American Bird Conservancy and the National Audubon Society as cooperating partners implementing the program. The National Audubon Society, which eventually became BirdLife International's partner-designate in the United States, chose to implement the IBA Program on a state-by-state basis, with Pennsylvania becoming the first state to kick off a program (Crossley 1999). There are now about 46 IBA Programs in the U.S., and New York, Pennsylvania, Washington, North Carolina, Florida, and California have published inventories similar to this one.

As the IBA Program reached the shores of the U.S., the definition of what should be an IBA was expanding. The American Bird Conservancy and the National Audubon Society, the two early players in implementing the IBA Program, further defined the elements we were all seeking in these landscapes. It could be argued that BirdLife International's early attempts at identifying IBAs focused on those areas of greatest importance where staggering numbers of birds congregated, or the rarest species were found. There is no doubt in anyone's mind that these areas are critical, but it is also true that if we are to shepherd the 900 or so species of birds in North America (and other species on other continents) then intelligently managing the few areas where enormous numbers of birds (usually waterbirds) congregate will not be enough. We need to account for the life history needs of all the species we are concerned about, from breeding through migration and then to over-wintering.

Those implementing the IBA Program began to conceive of IBA sites in a hierarchy. All IBAs will eventually be ranked as either globally, continentally, or locally important. With this structure in mind, thresholds were developed for each criterion to determine where a particular IBA would fit in the rankings. For example, 1,000 raptors using a site in a given season might warrant recognition of the site as an IBA at the state level; 15,000 raptors would trigger a continental IBA; and the occurrence of more than 1 percent of the global population of a raptor species, a global IBA.[1] It is the task of the Nevada IBA Program to identify IBAs of state level significance, and data from these sites will be evaluated by a National Technical Committee to determine whether continental or global thresholds are met. This wider latitude in defining IBAs also gives each state the flexibility to craft the criteria into a form that has the most relevance to local conservation. This element was critical in Nevada for reasons that are discussed below under the headings of "Context: The Nevada Landscape" and "Definition of a Nevada IBA."

As in other countries, the IBA Program has met with great success in the United States. In many states excellent progress has been made towards improving the management of these landscapes for birds (National Audubon Society 2004a).

Snowy Egret

Both Washington and New York states have passed legislation giving IBAs higher priority for conservation measures. The New York IBA Program helped secure $2.5 million of Land and Water Conservation Funds for habitat acquisition and restoration. The North Carolina IBA Program orchestrated the purchase of coastal lands critical to colonial shorebirds. The Montana IBA Program has made great conservation strides in protecting and managing a large tract of cottonwood forest near Kalispell. These are but a few national examples.

In Nevada, the IBA Program has engaged in more than an inventory of sensitive lands. We have initiated conservation work on the Carson River Delta IBA, one of the first areas the program recognized. We have collaborated extensively with conservation partners to devise management plans and engage in

[1]More recently, the figure of one percent of a geographic population has been identified as the threshold for global and continental IBAs.

conservation planning for some of our sensitive lands that include IBAs. We have also developed avitourism opportunities across the state, particularly in rural Nevada.

Context: The Nevada Landscape

The Great Basin ecoregion covers most of the state of Nevada, although the Mojave, Sierra Nevada, and Columbia Plateau ecoregions are also represented within the borders. To any traveler crossing Nevada along US 50 or I-80, the state is stark and the aridity unsettling. What these two transects tend to cloak is that there is actually a reasonable amount of variation in the precipitation pattern across the state. Precipitation in Nevada varies somewhat with latitude, but primarily by altitude. The higher mountains tend to receive and retain more of a snow pack that in some locations supports perennial streams and riparian areas and even reaches valley floors to sustain wetlands and open waters. The Sierra Nevada barely intrude into the western edge of the state, but they average about 60 - 80 inches of precipitation each year. This falls mostly as snow, and some of this moisture eventually reaches Important Bird Areas (IBAs) such as Pyramid Lake, Lahontan Valley Wetlands, and (ostensibly) Walker Lake as runoff. The Sierra Nevada also create a tremendous rain shadow, and it isn't until one reaches the eastern side of the state that the effects of this shadow start to moderate. Ranges like the Ruby and Jarbidge Mountains generally capture a respectable amount of snow, and the northeastern part of the state is usually greener to the eye of the traveler than most other parts of the state. In general, most of the state receives less than 10 inches of rain annually, with some higher elevations receiving 20 - 40 inches.

Nevada is the most mountainous state in the U.S. Though they are moving slowly enough to allow an accurate count, the exact number of ranges has avoided consensus. Wuerthner (1992) reported 160 named major ranges, with numerous lesser hills and high points, many unnamed, all of which totaled up to 314 ranges (McLane 1978). All of this variation in elevation means that it is possible to travel from the lowest point on the Colorado River (479 feet) to the highest point on Boundary Peak (13,140 feet) and pass from the Mojave Desert through numerous life zones ending in Alpine terrain.

Given this variation in precipitation and altitude, the variety of habitats comes as no surprise to the visitor who leaves any of the asphalt arteries traversing the state. The wide assortment of habitats supports a diverse bird community. Add in the fact that Nevada lies in the Pacific Flyway and the record of over 473 species in the state may come as no surprise.

As the driest state in the nation, Nevada's unique landscape presents unusual challenges to the IBA model. Consider the basis of the IBA Program as formulated by BirdLife International, whereby IBAs may be selected on the basis of unusually large congregations of target species. With few exceptions, the resources Nevada offers to birds are available in a widely dispersed, low density pattern, and the distribution of birds reflects the distribution of these resources. That does not mean that Nevada is not important to birds—the state has significant responsibility for a suite of sagebrush and piñon-juniper dependent species such as Greater Sage-Grouse, Pinyon Jay, Brewer's Sparrow, Sage Thrasher, and Sage Sparrow. Nevada also has a few sites that concentrate birds in significant numbers, and one of these sites, Lahontan Valley, is part of the Western Hemispheric Shorebird Reserve Network (Manomet Center for Conservation Science 2004). But more often than not defining Important Bird Areas for Nevada's species of concern requires identifying large landscapes with good quality habitat, even if the overall densities of birds within the IBA do not match the hundreds of thousands of shorebirds that congregate at places like Utah's Great Salt Lake.

Definition of a Nevada IBA

IBA programs at both the national and state level are assisted by Technical Advisory Committees (TACs). In the case of state level TACs, regional experts are assembled to provide insight and guidance for the programs. One of the first tasks assigned to the Nevada IBA TAC was to devise the criteria that would make the IBA Program relevant to the Nevada landscape. To develop these criteria the TAC consulted two primary sources of information. As is the practice, the criteria established by BirdLife International were adopted but the global thresholds modified to permit the identification of state level IBAs. This generally meant lowering threshold numbers, for example as described above using the case of raptors. A rule of thumb used by at least some IBA Programs is that the goal is to capture the top 10 percent of the sites available to birds in the state. With this general guideline in mind and using the TAC's knowledge of bird populations in Nevada, we identified threshold numbers that we believed would define the top 10 percent of the state's landscapes for birds. Adapting BirdLife International's IBA criteria also meant bringing Nevada's specific habitats into the mix. For example, both aspen forests and alpine habitats are limited in extent in Nevada, making their importance to maintaining certain bird species disproportionate to their geographic extent.

As the Nevada IBA Program began, 36 other states already had programs under way. The committee also examined the criteria adopted by those states and considered their merit in Nevada. It was largely through evaluation of state level criteria that the Nevada IBA Program adopted two supplemental criteria: NV-4, sites supporting long-term avian research efforts; and NV-5, sites providing important, bird-specific educational opportunities. While some of the reviewed states had adopted these as stand-alone criteria, they were controversial as they encouraged a drift away from the original core goals of the international IBA program. The Nevada IBA TAC felt that these elements could be important and would consider these contributing elements to a site nomination which otherwise met one or more of the more rigorous bird abundance or habitat quality based criteria. The TAC also recognized that only one site in Nevada—the Goshute Mountains—had supported any activity that could be considered long-term research. HawkWatch International has been counting migrating raptors moving along the spine of the Goshutes for more than 20 years.

Least Bittern

One of the first challenges the Nevada IBA TAC faced was to determine which species of birds would form the basis of **Criterion NV-1** (sites important to species of concern in Nevada) and the program's focus. Many states maintain a list of species of concern that includes birds, but Nevada was not among those states. However, the *Nevada Partners in Flight Bird Conservation Plan* (Neel 1999) had been recently published when the TAC was evaluating in 2001 how to identify a suitable suite of birds. The bird conservation plan is based on a list of 51 species compiled after an exhaustive review process. To derive this list of species, the Nevada Partners in Flight Working Group evaluated each of the variables listed below for each candidate to the list (Neel 1999, pp. 18-19):

- **Colorado Bird Observatory Total Score.** A numeric index formulated by the observatory using ranking factors similar to those used by numerous state Natural Heritage programs.
- **Endangered Species Act.** Species which are listed or proposed for listing as federally Threatened or Endangered.
- **Habitat Threat.** Demonstrable evidence of historic, ongoing, or future threats to the nesting, migratory, or wintering habitat.
- **Importance of Area.** Based on an examination of the distribution of this species, Nevada provides a large percentage of the total nesting habitat, and therefore a high degree of stewardship responsibility for the well-being of the species.

- **Low Numbers or Isolated Population.** Geographical isolation of Nevada's nesting population and/or a low nesting population in the state.
- **Population Decline.** The species has demonstrated an alarming downward population trend in the state.
- **Uniquely Representative of a Habitat Type.** Species selected because they epitomized an otherwise poorly represented habitat type, or for their ability to respond positively to habitat improvements.
- **Umbrella Species.** Management for a species in this category would address the needs of a larger community of species.
- **Unknown.** The ecological needs, population densities, or distributions of species in this category are intractable, and by their nature raise a red flag for conservation concerns.

The Nevada IBA TAC chose to add the list of federally Endangered or Threatened species of birds to this list of Nevada Partners in Flight (PIF) species. In large part this was a perfunctory gesture, as Western Yellow-billed Cuckoo and Southwestern Willow Flycatcher already occupied the Nevada PIF list. Other species attributed to Nevada from the Threatened and Endangered species list constituted accidental occurrences and would not alone form the basis for an IBA.

Criterion NV-2, "a site harboring an assemblage of species restricted to a unique or threatened natural community," was also a carry over criterion from BirdLife International that received some tailoring for Nevada. As previously mentioned, Nevada's environment is a uniquely challenging place to work, and what constitutes a unique or threatened natural community here is context specific. A particular type of habitat could be abundant and in good condition in other states, but for the purpose of sustaining our own bird populations some of these same communities warranted examination. To warrant recognition under this criterion, a site had to have both high quality habitat (that alone making it unique) *and* the appropriate bird community in residence. Shear numbers of birds were not necessarily required, merely a largely intact and representative community.

Two habitat types recognized as either unique or threatened in Nevada are the alpine zone and wetlands. Alpine habitat is restricted to the tops of the highest peaks in the state where elevation promotes a weather pattern more similar to areas thousands of miles to the north. However, with only a couple of minor exceptions, these areas do not have the attendant bird community one typically associates with the alpine community. Explanations remain unresearched, but one hypothesis is that these islands of habitat are too small and widely separated to sustain populations of these birds.

Another habitat type of great interest in Nevada is wetlands. An estimate based on the National Wetlands Inventory indicates about 1.5 percent of Nevada's present surface area is vegetated wetlands or open water (E. Skudlarek, Nevada Natural Heritage Program, pers. comm. 2004). This represents about half of Nevada's historic wetlands, as another estimate suggests about 52 percent of the state's wetlands have been lost since settlement (Dahl and Johnson 1991). What makes these statistics so vital is that although extremely small in total area, riparian communities in this region are critical centers of biodiversity (Mac 1988). More than 75 percent of the species in the region are strongly associated with riparian vegetation (U.S. General Accounting Office 1993), including 80 percent of the birds (Dobkin 1998). Every drop of water in Nevada is precious to something.

Criterion NV-3 focuses on sites where significant congregations of birds occur. This, too, is a criterion easily recognized from BirdLife International's IBA approach. However, thresholds in this criterion have been lowered from global levels to be relevant at the state level. The criterion covers the species typically recognized as congregatory—waterfowl, shorebirds, gulls and terns, wading birds, and raptors (in migration). It also covers song birds in migration, which are not typically thought of as congregatory but may occur in significant concentrations where migration bottlenecks occur. This category also recognizes that birds may occur in unusually high numbers and that such areas may be identified on the basis of comparison to other known populations across the state. The detailed criteria adopted for Nevada are included in this volume as Appendix II.

While the Nevada IBA Program concerned itself with scaling criteria and identifying thresholds that would be relevant for the western Great Basin and northern Mojave Desert, the national and global IBA efforts honed criteria for larger geographic scales. The National Technical Committee took as one of its first tasks the identification of which birds and how many of these birds would be required to identify a globally- or continentally-significant aggregation of birds. The species relevant to Nevada's IBAs, and the thresholds identified, are listed in Appendix III.

Evaluating IBAs to determine whether they meet state, continental, or global thresholds is the duty of two separate entities. At the state level, the Nevada Technical Advisory Committee determines whether state thresholds are met. Higher level designations are determined by a National Technical Committee. This body is faced with a daunting task, given the thousands of IBAs they must review. At the time this book is being prepared, a higher level review has not been performed for any of the Nevada IBAs. It is worth noting that the threshold numbers provided by the National Technical Committee have not been used in Nevada to fuel the search for IBAs. There is excellent overlap in the species listed in the National Technical Committee's table and the list of species identified by the Nevada IBA TAC; it is really the global and continental threshold numbers that constitute new information. This information was received as this manuscript was in preparation, so one of the future tasks of the Nevada IBA Program may be to take another pass at identifying critical landscapes and nominating new IBAs based on their potential to hold critical populations of these species.

Coordination

Collaboration and partnerships have always been the hallmark of the IBA Program. A number of ongoing conservation efforts in Nevada dovetail with the IBA Program to varying degrees, offering opportunities for partnerships. A few of the more pertinent programs are discussed below in the context of how these programs have interacted with the IBA Program.

Great Basin Bird Observatory

At the time the IBA Program started in Nevada, the Great Basin Bird Observatory, under the direction of Dr. Ted Floyd, was wrapping up field work for the first-ever breeding bird atlas for the state. Ted did a remarkable job of locating and coordinating over 400 volunteers to canvas the state, conducting breeding bird censuses in randomly selected plots.

To assist the Nevada IBA Program, Ted permitted access to the raw data collected for the atlas. In several cases atlas data were critical for supplementing nominations for IBAs. In this book, Nevada Breeding Bird Atlas data are reported in the site descriptions in a density format, for example, as "1 - 4 pairs/km^2."

The Nature Conservancy

The Nature Conservancy (TNC) has been engaged in a process of conservation planning at the landscape level. The resulting documents are ecoregion plans, and they synthesize a tremendous amount of information gathered and analyzed to help TNC prioritize the areas in which they will focus their conservation efforts. Birds constitute one of many variables that go into selecting these priority landscapes, and boundaries are determined by the suite of species distinguishing the landscape and are not specific to bird conservation. Thus the IBA process and TNC ecoregion planning efforts are compatible but different approaches to conservation planning. The Great Basin ecoregion plan formed a valuable starting point for identifying potential IBAs, though these sites were nominated only as quantitative bird data became available.

Governor's Sage Grouse Planning Initiative

The U.S. Fish and Wildlife Service (USFWS) has received seven petitions to list the Greater Sage-Grouse as Threatened or Endangered under the Endangered Species Act. Recognizing the dramatic social and economic impacts such a listing could bring, Governor Guinn of Nevada encouraged a statewide planning effort designed to identify and implement coordinated management at a grassroots level that should lead to the enhancement of sage grouse populations.

The Nevada Sage Grouse Conservation Strategy was completed in October of 2001 and marked the beginning of the Local Area Conservation Planning phase of the Greater Sage-Grouse Conservation Plan for Nevada and Eastern California. (NDOW 2004)

This planning effort was already well under way when the Nevada IBA Program began. Largely because of capacity constraints, the IBA Program has not participated directly in this effort, but the Lahontan Audubon Society has been an active participant throughout the process. The IBA Program has been highly supportive of the effort and encouraged by the progress made to date.

American Bird Conservancy

The American Bird Conservancy (ABC) and the National Audubon Society kicked off the U.S. Important Bird Areas Program together in 1995. In the late 1990s the paths of these programs diverged and, while National Audubon continued to implement the IBA Program on behalf of BirdLife International, the ABC pursued their own parallel program. ABC's Important Bird Areas Program has concentrated on identifying and documenting upper echelon sites throughout all 50 states, that is, those of significance on a global level (American Bird Conservancy 2004). One of the results of ABC's efforts has been an excellent book on their IBA Program and the IBAs they identified (Chipley 2003). ABC's Important Bird Areas coordinator provided valuable insight into their early efforts in Nevada, and this input came prior to the publication of Chipley (2003) and at the start of the Nevada IBA Program.

Other State IBA Programs

Because birds do not recognize the arbitrary political boundaries that define states, coordinating efforts with adjacent IBA programs was critical. Aside from soliciting professional support, this effort attempted to prevent IBA boundaries from simply stopping at state borders when appropriate habitat and bird populations clearly extended beyond. In some cases this worked, in others it did not. For example, the Idaho IBA Program is evaluating the Owyhee Uplands as a potential IBA. The Nevada program has been equally interested in the South Fork of the Owyhee River, which flows into Idaho's proposed IBA. However, data are lacking for the Nevada portion of this IBA and as a consequence the area has yet to be nominated or evaluated. Because state level criteria do vary, it is possible to end up with an IBA that ends at a state border, simply because the birds of concern in one state do not overlap sufficiently with the adjacent state to meet the minimum IBA criteria.

Other National Bird Conservation Efforts

The North American Bird Conservation Initiative (NABCI 2005) incorporates several conservation plans. These plans include the North American Waterfowl Management Plan, the United States Shorebird Conservation Plan, the Partners In Flight North American Landbird Conservation Plan, and the North American Waterbird Conservation Plan. This list does not touch on the various interest groups focused on game species or the long-standing efforts of state and federal wildlife management agencies.

The Nevada IBA Program participates in these initiatives as opportunities arise. In addition to Partners In Flight, the Intermountain West Joint Venture has been particularly active in the state and integral in developing funding opportunities for on-the-ground conservation efforts. The Joint Ventures are active to varying degrees across the country, but essentially are developed to support and implement thethe the North American Waterfowl Management Plan. Understandably, the Joint Ventures' initial efforts focused on improving waterfowl habitat but more recently have shifted to an all-bird effort.

National Audubon and some state Audubon chapters are also participating through the IBA Program in some of the other national bird conservation efforts. The IBA Program contributes to NABCI by identifying the most important sites at which to implement large-scale conservation efforts to ensure the protection of all bird species in all habitats. Audubon has agreements with two of the NABCI partners (the U.S. Shorebird Conservation Plan and the North American Waterbird Conservation Plan) to identify IBAs throughout the country that support significant shorebird and waterbird populations. Audubon also works in cooperation with Partners in Flight to identify IBAs that are critical for landbirds. (National Audubon Society 2004b)

Conservation and Management of IBAs

This book is designed to formalize the identification of IBAs in Nevada and to identify primarily landscape level conservation concerns on each IBA. However, the actions needed to conserve Nevada IBAs will not happen just because this book has been published. Ideally, this book and the effort that led up to it will be a means to an end, whether it motivates a citizen-scientist to volunteer to monitor an IBA, or an advocate to work for informed stewardship of an IBA, or a land owner to consider how their land will be managed in perpetuity to benefit birds and other wildlife. The recognition of IBAs is intended to help birds and the broader suite of wildlife under their umbrella by setting science-based priorities for habitat conservation and promoting positive action to safeguard vital bird habitats (National Audubon Society 2004b).

The two Audubon Chapters in Nevada have wide interests and varied programs. All of these efforts are important, but it is certainly the hope of the National Audubon Society that IBAs will become rallying points for chapter conservation efforts and will form the focus of future programs. Certainly IBAs can accommodate a significant portion of ongoing chapter programs, from field trips to education to on-the-ground restoration efforts. Another as yet untested approach to IBA conservation in Nevada is the "adopt an IBA program." Other states have successfully linked IBAs with Audubon chapters and similar stakeholder groups. These groups then assume responsibility for monitoring, developing projects, and advocating for these landscapes.

The Important Bird Areas Program is not a regulatory initiative and the program places no restrictions on land use or activities. Without regulatory authority, the IBA Program seeks other strategies based on mutually beneficial partnerships and cooperation with landowners and managers. The program also provides a basis for setting priorities for public and private conservation activities. Important Bird Area status gives focus to activities such as bird and habitat monitoring, habitat management, exotic species removal, education, and advocacy. Data generated through the Important Bird Areas process can inform natural resource planning, land use, habitat protection, and habitat management.

It is Audubon's hope that the Important Bird Areas Program will facilitate a positive and constructive dialogue between private landowners, public and private land managers, policy makers, birders, and citizens that will result in the long-term conservation of habitats for birds.

IBAs provide excellent opportunities for building successful partnerships. Nevada is unique in that about 90 percent of its lands are publicly owned. Although many IBAs have been defined entirely within public lands, private land owners are also responsible for critical wildlife habitat. To a large extent this land distribution pattern is an artifact of mid-nineteenth century settlement patterns and the method in which homesteads and land patents were granted. Essentially, floodplains and riparian areas best suited settlers' needs in this arid environment better than the drier uplands, so in most cases these areas remain in private ownership and are often the focus of agricultural operations in rural areas. Some of these areas in turn were incorporated into IBAs, generally where the private landowner has demonstrated exemplary stewardship skills. These IBAs provide opportunities to bring interested, capable, and cooperative land managers from diverse backgrounds to the table to talk about enhancements that can benefit everyone.

This book is the result of the initial identification phase of the Nevada IBA Program. However, significant gaps exist in our understanding of the temporal and geographic distribution and abundance of birds across Nevada's landscape. Various efforts are underway to increase our knowledge of birds in Nevada, and as more is known it is likely that more landscapes will need to be evaluated for IBA status.

Aspen grove in the Carson Range IBA

Conservation of Important Bird Areas

The IBA Program provides a mechanism for prioritizing landscapes for conservation. Having reached a milestone with the conclusion of the first round of nominations and the publication of this book, the two state Audubon chapters in Nevada and the National Audubon Society now have a blueprint for conservation in the state and a selection of key sites where on-the-ground efforts may now be focused.

That said, it is important to understand that IBA recognition is not the answer to every conservation concern. The IBA model is best suited to rare and congregatory species. Conversely, it is not particularly well suited to species that occur in low numbers and low densities throughout their life cycle, or at least through the part of their life cycles that occur while they are in Nevada. The Northern Goshawk, a species that is solitary and maintains large territories, is one example. Two more examples are Pinyon Jay and Three-toed Woodpecker. Both of these species tend to be irruptive and may be common in one place one year, only to disappear entirely the next, based on bumper crops of piñon nuts or pine bark beetle infestations, respectively.

When reviewing Nevada's IBA map it is worth keeping these points in mind. It is also worth considering that the *lack* of IBA status for a particular place can mean many things. First, it can mean that the site has not been nominated and evaluated for IBA status. Second, the lack of IBA status may simply mean that the suite of birds characterizing the site do not lend themselves to management under a site-based conservation approach (Cullinan 2001). Focusing all future bird conservation efforts solely on Important Bird Areas will not assure the perpetuation of all bird species in the state. Think of this portfolio as a place to start, and the core of the habitat that those interested in bird conservation in Nevada must steward.

The ultimate goal of the Important Bird Areas Program at every location on every continent is to facilitate the long-term management of these landscapes for the benefit of the birds that define the landscapes. Recognition of a landscape as an IBA does not confer any kind of regulatory status. Rather, the Important Bird Areas Program looks to balance the needs and goals of landowners and land managers with the needs of the birds at the site. Ideally, the needs of all the stakeholders can be met without serious compromise and with beneficial outcomes for all involved.

The model for successful conservation of IBAs is based on partnerships among stakeholders willing to come to the table and work collaboratively. In Nevada the IBA Program has already worked with the Natural Resources Conservation Service, USFWS, Bureau of Land Management (BLM), Bureau of Reclamation, Nevada Division of State Parks, and the Nevada Department of Wildlife Management to bring positive change to critical landscapes. Near-term challenges faced by the Nevada IBA Program include identifying stakeholders for each of the IBAs, identifying appropriate projects for enhancement or restoration, and building successful partnerships to accomplish those tasks.

Another task at hand is monitoring. Monitoring has been a critical element of the Important Bird Areas Program nearly from the start. In the United States, considerable discussion swirls around exactly what form this effort should take. The purposes of monitoring, to step back a bit from that previous question, are many. One goal is to build a coalition of citizen-scientists who will adopt these landscapes and begin to develop a sense of propriety for their well being. Another need is to track long-term trends in bird populations at each site. And a spin-off of this last element, simply having someone on the site at least on an occasional basis, will allow a broad assessment of site condition and what management actions are needed.

Each IBA nomination form included a space for recording information regarding threats to the site. The threats to IBAs in Nevada are many and omnipresent, and although there are commonalities in the types of threats, they certainly vary in severity from site to site. Some of the more pressing and widespread issues are discussed below.

Water

Nevada is the driest state in the Nation, and during the course of the Nevada IBA Program a 500-year drought was declared (Webb 2004). A drought puts a strain on all water users, and while wildlife in the state is first in need for water, it is last– where it is counted at all– in water rights, often receiving none. Many demands are placed on this scarce resource and depending on the watershed may include residential and commercial needs, agricultural demands, and natural elements of the hydrological cycle including groundwater recharge and evaporation. This latter variable can be quite high in Nevada, where summer daytime temperature can break a 100°F (115°F in southern Nevada) and hot, dry winds are an almost daily occurrence.

At the root of our worst conservation crises is the lack of water. Walker Lake (IBA) is on the brink of ecological collapse because the Walker River is over-allocated by 140 percent and has been for more than 100 years. Upstream water

Walker Lake shoreline level in 1882, and today's lake visible in the distance

users represented by the Walker River Irrigation District have shown no interest in reaching a solution to this situation that would benefit the lake. In southern Nevada, commercial interests are pressing to mine groundwater and pipe the water to Las Vegas, a city that is the fastest growing metropolitan area in the country and also boasts the highest per capita water use of any city in the West (Soussan 2003). This groundwater pumping in a setting that is little studied and poorly understood could lead to the disappearance of seeps and springs critical to at least six IBAs.

Invasive or Noxious Plants

Probably every state and the federal government has regulatory language in place that tries to parse the distinctions between *invasive* and *noxious* plants. Invasive plants tend to be defined as those that are non-native to the ecosystem under consideration and that are capable of out-competing and crowding out other plants. This competition can be so lopsided that the result is a monoculture of the invading plant. Noxious weeds tend to be those that are harmful, and often this is defined in an economic and agricultural context. An argument could easily be put forward, however, that even those plants that do not cause immediate harm do create indirect but nonetheless measurable harm.

In spite or perhaps because of its harsh climate, Nevada is susceptible to invasion by many weeds. Tall whitetop (or perennial pepperweed) has invaded riparian systems in western Nevada and has formed extensive monocultures that are of little value to any species of bird, all at the cost of native habitat. Tamarisk (or salt cedar) and to a lesser degree, Russian olive are aggressive invaders in riparian systems in the Great Basin. Tamarisk forms monotypic stands to the detriment of native cottonwoods and willows. Once established, tamarisk has four detrimental impacts on natural ecosystems: increased soil salinity, increased water consumption, increased wildfire frequency, and increased frequency and intensity of flooding (Wiesenborn 1996). It is both incomprehensible and unforgivable that both of these latter two species are still available at landscape nurseries, though they readily escape cultivation to further aggravate habitat degradation of our native landscapes.

Another significant invader in the Nevada landscape is cheatgrass. This cool season annual grass emerges in mid-to-late winter and matures by late May or early June, at which point it senesces to become a tinder-dry, fire prone understory in desert shrub communities. Cheatgrass is aggressive and often out-competes native vegetation in an interesting but unfortunate cycle that involves fire and grazing. These processes are described below.

Fire

Where there is insufficient water then the opposite basic element, fire, can also be a problem. The nature of fire in Nevada is a bit more complex, and whether its occurrence is "good" or "bad" depends on several factors. Many of Nevada's habitat types are influenced by fire. Historically, sagebrush communities are believed to have burned on the frequency of once every 50 to 100 years as part of a natural cycle of renewal. Before agency policy was established to suppress all forest and range fires, fire played a critical role in regulating the extent of piñon-juniper forests. Fire also played a role in habitat structure in the Sierra Nevada forests and in the establishment and rejuvenation of aspen stands.

Restoring fire to the landscape is a complex problem. Variables include the fact that many landscapes are now loaded with so much combustible fuel as a result of decades of fire suppression that any fire would now be intense and devastating. Weeds and their relation to fire add another twist to the story. When cheatgrass ignites, either from lightning strikes or by human causes, it burns quickly and with great intensity. The seeds of cheatgrass are adapted to survive these fires and the grass quickly and vigorously resprouts the following year. In a few years' time cheatgrass stands rebuild fuel loads large enough to once again burn. Contrast this to the native desert shrub communities that are adapted to burn on 50 to 100 year cycles. The three-year fire return interval prevents the native shrub community from reestablishing itself, and the result is a cheatgrass monotype and the elimination of an entire community of sagebrush dependent species.

Hundreds of thousands of acres of native habitat in Nevada have been converted to weed-dominated landscapes with fire as the agent of change. When these burns occur, land managers need to rapidly re-seed the burned area in order to give native vegetation a competitive toehold against invasive exotics. The challenges are numerous, including finding and maintaining a stock of native seeds and applying the seeds to a vast landscape, often in places too steep or remote for mechanical seeding.

Grazing Management

The Great Basin presents an extremely challenging environment for livestock. With unpredictable rainfall, there are some years, and sometimes many years in succession, where the land can not produce sufficient forage to provide for the needs of livestock and wildlife. A rancher tied to land and place does not have the luxury of simply selling his entire herd and waiting for the next good rain year, so stocking rates can and have exceeded what the land can bear. Cattle grazing predominates in Nevada, but in places sheep are grazed as well. Add to this mix herds of wild horses which are not native to the landscape and which the BLM struggles to find the resources to manage.

Excessive grazing pressure impacts Great Basin habitats in a variety of ways. In desert shrub communities, excessive grazing tends to result in a community dominated by shrubs and lacking in grasses and forbs (broad-leafed plants collectively referred to as "wildflowers"). Grazers can also encourage the dominance and spread of cheatgrass and certain other weeds by passively distributing seeds and by selectively eating more palatable native plants and thereby reducing the ability of natives to compete with non-natives. These changes in community structure and composition can be detrimental to Greater Sage-Grouse and other native sagebrush obligates whose life history requirements are complex and specific.

There are ranchers in the state who are doing an exemplary job managing their herds under difficult circumstances. Some have done such an outstanding job of balancing the needs of maintaining their own economic viability against the needs of the land that their properties have qualified as Important Bird Areas.

Habitat Conversion and Development

Development, whether commercial or residential, leads to one form of habitat conversion. In spite of appearing to be a largely rural state, Nevada is actually the most urbanized state in the nation. What this statistic means is that a higher percentage of the state's residents live in an urbanized setting than do people in any other state. Nevada has two urban areas, Reno and the far larger Las Vegas area. Sprawl is rampant in both communities. The IBA most directly threatened by development is the Carson Valley IBA. This idyllic setting has attracted a lot of lifestyle refugees and people attracted to the pace of life and setting of the valley. As a result farms and open space are rapidly being converted to housing developments and ranchettes.

Other types of habitat conversion are driven by the previously discussed fire cycles, where landscape level conversions from native vegetation to invasive non-native plants can happen rapidly. Agricultural operations can also act as rapid agents of change when native vegetation is converted to agricultural crops, or conversely when irrigated hay meadows or alfalfa fields (the latter used by many birds, especially White-faced Ibis) are taken out of rotation and left to fallow. Without management intervention this latter step tends to result in weed invasions.

Off-road Vehicle Use

Off-road vehicles (ORVs) are booming in popularity as a form of recreation. Land management agencies have been nearly blind-sided by this form of recreation and only now are starting to grapple with how to manage this force. While many riders are responsible and stay on established roads, others choose to strike out on their own and go cross-country. Some of the consequences of this behavior are proliferation of unauthorized roads that can lead to serious erosion problems, destruction of vegetation and habitat, direct disruption of animal behavior, and habitat fragmentation. Even where ORV use is expressly prohibited, unauthorized use occurs and enforcement of laws is often a problem for agencies that are chronically under-staffed and over-worked.

Snake Valley below the Northern Snake Range IBA

The problem of off-road vehicles extends to watercraft, particularly jet skis, as well. This little-regulated form of recreation can also lead to disruption of wildlife when users spook resting birds or venture too close to sensitive nesting areas. Some sites which might otherwise offer good bird habitat have been lost because they are too frequently disturbed by jet skiers. One example of such a site is Bowman Reservoir on the northeast edge of the Lower Muddy River IBA.

This brief description encapsulates the nature of the conservation challenges facing the management of many IBAs. These are some of the more common problems facing IBAs in Nevada. This list is by no means comprehensive and avoids many of the complexities associated with these issues.

Reading the IBA Accounts

Each site in Nevada identified as an Important Bird Area is described on the following pages. The sites are presented in alphabetical order, with the frontispiece map providing an overview of the state and showing site locations. The information in the site descriptions is derived primarily from the IBA nominations, though published and unpublished literature helped complete the description of some sites. Full references for these cited works are included in the back of this book. A brief description of the information you will encounter under each site report follows below.

Following the title of the IBA, each site description begins with basic geography, including the area and location of the site. The **area** is given in hectares (ha) and is derived from mapping initiated for the project by a GIS class at the University of Nevada, Reno. This number is useful for comparative purposes among the different Nevada IBAs, but keep in mind that it is not a precise number, in that borders are approximate and not based on boundary lines established by a civil engineer with a theodolite. The **location**, given in Universal Transverse Mercator (UTM) coordinates (North American Datum 1927), identifies the approximate center of the IBA.

Next follows the site **description**. The text of the description is meant to provide an overview of the IBA with an emphasis on land forms, major physiography, and the primary vegetation types that characterize the habitats available to birds. Historical or cultural information about the site may also be included if the information is believed to be of general interest or has influenced the way birds use the site. Principal land uses on the site are also provided under this heading.

Following the site description is information on the IBA's **birds**. The initial information presented in this section is broadly descriptive and explains how the IBA is used by birds. This is followed by a table of data upon which the IBA determination was based; it includes the species of interest, year and season of data collection, the number of birds recorded, and the proposed and confirmed criteria with which each species' occurrence was reviewed. The numbers presented in this table are typically *peak* numbers reported at the site. In an effort to use current data, an emphasis was placed on finding data collected within five years of the submission of the IBA nomination. This was not always possible. Often the remoteness of rural Nevada limits the frequency of site visits, and the wide fluctuation in rainfall means some sites experience high bird numbers only rarely. The confirmed criteria used to define the site are listed, as are proposed criteria that are awaiting further review or the availability of additional data.

Next follows a discussion of **conservation issues**. The stressors listed in this section were identified in the site nomination, though some updating of the material has occurred where additional information was available. The landscape is dynamic and change is a given constant. Unfortunately, rather than coming and going, threats tend to accumulate and interact, so the identified list of threats at each site may be conservative estimates.

Each site description concludes with a section titled **visiting the site**, where brief advice regarding access to the site is offered. Not all sites are readily accessible, and some, primarily due to ownership, are not accessible at all to the public. Before visiting any IBA, the reader is asked to review Appendix IV, titled "Important *Birding* Areas?" Above all, this is a plea to respect the rights of private landowners who may not wish to host bird watchers, however friendly to birds their management practices are.

Observing Greater Sage-Grouse at a lek site

Nevada's Important Bird Areas

Ash Meadows National Wildlife Refuge

Area: 9,921 ha
UTM Easting: 561860
UTM Northing: 4030191

Description

Ash Meadows National Wildlife Refuge (NWR) was established by the U.S. Fish and Wildlife Service in June of 1984 with the help of TNC and the BLM. The refuge is located about 90 miles northwest of Las Vegas in the Amargosa Valley of southern Nye County, at the Nevada-California border. Over 22,000 acres of spring-fed wetlands and alkaline desert uplands are included. The refuge was set aside for the benefit of 13 Threatened and Endangered species and also provides habitat for at least 24 plants and animals found nowhere else in the world. (U.S. Fish and Wildlife Service 2004a)

The refuge is a major discharge point for a vast underground aquifer system stretching 100 miles to the northeast. Water-bearing strata comes to the surface and produces more than 30 seeps and springs that provide rich and complex habitats. Over 10,000 gallons per minute flow year-round, most of which comes from 7 major springs: Fairbanks, Rogers, Longstreet, Crystal, Point of Rocks, Jackrabbit, and Big Springs. The water arriving at Ash Meadows is called fossil water because it is believed to have entered the ground water system as much as 10,000 years ago. Many stream channels and wetlands are scattered throughout the area. Mesquite and ash tree groves flourish near the wetlands, and saltbush and creosote shrubs grow in drier upland soils. (U.S. Fish and Wildlife Service 2004a)

Ash Meadows was intensively farmed prior to its establishment as a National Wildlife Refuge. During the 1960s and early 1970s in particular, irrigated row crops, grazing, and development took a heavy toll on the area's natural resources. Plants, fish, and wildlife declined as pumping, diversion of spring channels, development of roads, large scale earth moving, and introduction of over 100 non-native plants and animals occurred in a blink of evolutionary time.

The Carson Slough, an area in the northwestern portion of the refuge which was historically the largest wetland in southern Nevada, was drained and mined for its peat in the 1960s.

The refuge is currently in the habitat restoration stage and will likely remain so for years to come. The overall goal of the refuge and its recovery plan for Threatened and Endangered species is to restore the area to its natural historic condition. This will involve redirecting spring outflows back into former natural channels, restoring wetlands, removing non-native species (particularly tamarisk, bass, tropical fish, and crayfish), restoring native riparian and upland vegetation, and removing unnecessary structures such as roads, fences, and power lines. (U.S. Fish and Wildlife Service 2004b)

Ash Meadows NWR has also been recognized as a Ramsar Wetland of International Importance (Ramsar 2005).

Birds

Two routes offer perennial surface water and cover for birds migrating through the western Great Basin. Ash Meadows and Oasis Valley form the southern end of one of those routes, while Pahranagat Valley Complex IBA to the east of Amaragosa Valley forms the other route. Collectively these two valleys probably support a significant portion of the passerines migrating into or through the western Great Basin. Like the Oasis Valley IBA, which lies a short flight northwest of Ash Meadows, many thousands of warblers have been documented using Ash Meadows in migration. Two endangered species success stories, the Peregrine Falcon and Bald Eagle, also use Ash Meadows seasonally

Winter at Ash Meadows NWR IBA

as a migration stopover. In addition to migrants, a few pairs of Southwestern Willow Flycatchers use Ash Meadows as breeding habitat from June through August each year.

Over 239 different species of birds have been recorded on the refuge. Fall and especially spring migration periods produce the greatest diversity and numbers. Spring migration usually occurs during April and May, and fall migration from mid-August through September. During the winter, marshes and reservoirs support the largest variety of water birds. Mesquite and ash tree groves at refuge headquarters and Point of Rocks harbor resident and migratory birds year-round, including typical Southwestern species such as Crissal Thrasher, Verdin, Phainopepla, and Lucy's Warbler. (U.S. Fish and Wildlife Service 2004b)

Species used to identify Ash Meadows NWR IBA and the criteria met by the site. Proposed criteria will be evaluated by the Nevada IBA TAC pending the availability of additional data. Proposed and confirmed codes are discussed in Appendix II.

Species	Year	Season	Min	Max	Units	Proposed	Confirmed
Loggerhead Shrike	2001	winter	-	22	individuals		NV1
Sage Sparrow	2000	winter	-	80	individuals		NV1
Wilson's Warbler	2001	migration	-	10,000	adults only	NV3g	NV1, NV2, NV3f
Southwest Willow Flycatcher	1998	breeding	6	10	adults only	NV3g	NV1, NV2
White-faced Ibis	2002	migration	211	439	individuals		NV1, NV3e
Phainopepla	2002	breeding,winter	-	50	individuals		NV1
Lucy's Warbler	2002	breeding	-	100	individuals		NV1
Yellow-breasted Chat	2002	breeding	-	60	individuals		NV1
Blue Grosbeak	2002	breeding	-	100	individuals		NV1
Waterfowl (22 species)	2001	all	22,995	29,770	individuals		NV3a
Waders & shorebirds (33 species)	2001	migration	1,512	2,118	individuals		NV3e, NV3c

Conservation Issues

The U.S. Fish and Wildlife Service is performing extensive restoration on the refuge. Non-native plants and animals will be removed to allow native plants and animals to thrive without competition (U.S. Fish and Wildlife Service 2004a). Access for visitors is also being improved and additional educational opportunities (e.g., kiosks) will be added.

Possibly the most critical issue looming over this and other IBAs in southern Nevada involves groundwater pumping. Las Vegas is constantly seeking additional sources of water to feed the rampant growth of the city. In 2004, the Lincoln County Conservation, Recreation, and Development Act passed Congress and facilitated water mining efforts in that county on behalf of Las Vegas and the Southern Nevada Water Authority (SNWA). Like giant straws, the pipelines will reach out in search of the same aquifers that likely feed critical springs, seeps, creeks, and rivers. Other county-based public land acts loom and similar outcomes may be expected. Most conservation organizations joined the battle over the Lincoln County act. There is no doubt that bill constituted only the first battle in a long water war.

Visiting the Site

The refuge welcomes visitors and has an ever-improving visitor access program. Several of the ponds and water impoundments are easily accessible with good viewing opportunities. The boardwalk behind refuge headquarters provides an excellent stroll through a mesquite forest and riparian stringer, ending at one of the impressive crystal blue springs at the refuge. The refuge also provides maps and information about current conditions at the site, and a refuge bird list is available at the headquarters and on line.

Ash Meadows NWR IBA is easily accessed from US 95. Turn south on NV 373 at Amargosa Valley and follow the signs to the refuge.

White-faced Ibis (© Richard S. Barrett)

Bilk Creek - Montana Mountains

Area: 256,038 ha
UTM Easting: 407374
UTM Northing: 4626214

Description

This large landscape in northwest Nevada is centered around one of the highest density Greater Sage-Grouse populations in the country (S. Stiver 2002, Nevada Division of Wildlife, pers. comm.). As part of an extensive landscape area, the site contains numerous habitat types including aspen, agricultural lands, and isolated riparian wetlands but is primarily characterized by sagebrush-steppe. The Bilk Creek and Montana Mountains are the two prominent ranges within the boundary. Ownership is primarily federal (BLM), but includes some private lands as well. Grasslands and sagebrush-steppe habitats are in good condition, though some isolated areas have been over-utilized. A large region in the Double H Mountains burned and is in danger of conversion to cheatgrass.

Land uses in the IBA include agriculture (private lands, permitted public lands, grazing and ranching, and associated infrastructure), seasonal hunting, and motorized and non-motorized recreation. The area is remote, the roads are mostly poor, and consequently the site receives little visitation.

Birds

The Bilk Creek-Montana Mountains IBA supports the largest Greater Sage-Grouse population in Nevada, one of the highest densities of Greater Sage-Grouse in the country. Other sagebrush obligate species are supported in what appears to be fairly high quality habitat, despite some localized areas impacted by over-utilization and an extensive burn at the southeast end of the site. Two of the observers in this area commented on the abundance and diversity of sparrows (ca. 8 species), though not all are on the PIF priority list.

Species used to identify Bilk Creek - Montana Mountains IBA and the criteria met by the site. Proposed Criteria are pending and will be evaluated by the National Technical Committee. Proposed/confirmed codes are discussed in Appendices II and III.

Species	Year	Season	Min	Max	Units	Proposed	Confirmed
Swainson's Hawk	1999	breeding	1	4	pairs/km^{2*}		NV1
Greater Sage-Grouse	2002	breeding	2,000	2,500	breeding pairs	A1	NV1, NV3g
Gray Flycatcher	2000	breeding	5	43	pairs/km^{2*}		NV1
Vesper Sparrow	2000	breeding	44	-	pairs/km^{2*}		NV1

*Density estimated in appropriate habitat and in the appropriate season.

Conservation Issues

This landscape is utilized at a fairly low rate, and currently there are no known plans to intensify (primarily agricultural) activities. Additional exploitation could alter habitat quality or quantity. As with most landscapes in the state, this one is at risk for large-scale conversion to annual grasses following catastrophic fires. Two such fires occurred in southern portions of the IBA, these were the Double H and Cherry Creek fires of 2000. The Winnemucca District of the BLM has either reseeded these areas or is in the process of doing so. Finally, ORV use and other types of recreation should be monitored carefully to avoid fragmentation and resource damage in the area.

Visiting the Site

Much of the wildlife in the area is concentrated along the Quinn River on the east side of the IBA and the King River Valley, which runs through the center of the IBA. Both of these areas contain significant amounts of private land. Viewing opportunities are primarily from the roads. The most accessible route skirts the east side of the IBA and includes US 95 between Orovada and McDermitt. Alternatively, a route departs from NV 140 at Sod House and heads north through the Kings River Valley, returning to NV 140 just south of Denio. Be aware that most roads in this IBA are in very poor shape and the possibility of getting stranded a long way from help is a distinct possibility.

Male Greater Sage-Grouse strut at a lek site

Boyd Humboldt Valley Wetlands

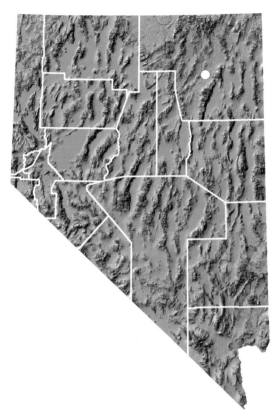

Area: 1,070 ha
UTM Easting: 628727
UTM Northing: 4530513

Description

The Boyd Humboldt Valley Wetlands are a rich lowland riparian wetland surrounded by sagebrush-steppe uplands. The floodplain and surrounding uplands provide critical summer, winter, and migration habitat for hundreds of bird species as well as many species of mammals, reptiles, and amphibians. The site is entirely in private ownership.

1871 priority water rights are used primarily for the production of native hay on this working ranch. Hardstem bullrush and cattail wetlands and native hay meadows are bisected by riparian woodlands dominated by sandbar willow. Surrounding uplands are composed of Wyoming sagebrush, green rabbitbrush, native bunchgrass, native forbs, as well as exotic crested wheatgrass, cheatgrass, and halogeton.

The principal feature of this landscape is the Humboldt River and a series of tributaries that irrigate a mile-wide floodplain through relatively dry, upland hill country. Extreme winter and summer temperatures from -50°F to 110°F have been recorded for the area. Annual precipitation averages 10-12 inches, mostly coming in the form of winter snow. River flows can vary significantly between seasons and can be as high as 4,000 cfs in spring to dry and ponded in late summer to 200 cfs and ice covered in winter.

This site also provides habitat for several other species of wildlife including foraging and possibly roosting habitat for 10-13 species of insectivorous bats and year-round habitat for the pygmy rabbit, dark kangaroo mouse, river otter, mink, and beaver, the latter acting as a keystone species in this desert riparian ecosystem.

Birds

The hay meadows on this IBA are used as foraging habitat for a mixed species colony of waterbirds (about 100 Snowy Egrets, 150 Black-crowned Night Herons, 20 Great Egrets, 20 Cattle Egrets), which nest in sandbar willow

Birders at an IBA dedication, Boyd Humboldt Valley Wetlands IBA

three miles downstream from the IBA. The IBA serves as nesting habitat for several raptor species (Swainson's Hawk, Short-eared Owl, Burrowing Owl, Long-Eared Owl, Great Horned Owl), wintering habitat for Bald Eagle, year-round habitat for thousands of individuals of 25 species of waterfowl, and seasonal habitat for thousands of individuals of 30 species of waterbirds and shorebirds. Some interesting oddities have shown up on the IBA over the years, and thanks to the interest and birding abilities of the ranch owner these rarities have not gone unnoticed. For example, in September of 2002 a male Vermillion Flycatcher visited the IBA, both unusually late and well out of range. In March 2004, four Lesser Sandhill Cranes appeared among the expected flock of Greater Sandhill Cranes on the site.

Species used to identify the Boyd Humboldt Valley Wetlands IBA and the criteria met by the site. Proposed Criteria are pending and will be evaluated by the National Technical Committee or the Nevada IBA TAC pending data availability. Proposed/confirmed codes are discussed in Appendices II and III.

Species	Year	Season	Min	Max	Units	Proposed	Confirmed
White-faced Ibis	2001	breeding	-	1500	adults only	NV3g	NV1, NV2, NV3e, NV3gv
Wilson's Phalarope	2001	breeding	-	5000	adults only	B1, NV3g	NV3e
Black Tern	2001	breeding	-	200	adults only	NV3g	NV3gv
Greater Sandhill Crane	2001	migration	300	600	adults only		NV1, NV3g
Long-billed Curlew	2001	breeding	-	40	adults only	A1, NV3g	NV1
Bobolink	2001	breeding	-	250	adults only	NV3g	NV1
Yellow-breasted Chat	2001	breeding	-	250	adults only	NV3g	NV1

Conservation Issues

The potential for an invasive species to become established is always a real threat. Tall whitetop is already established on site, but seasonal grazing seems to be keeping the species in check. Other species in the Humboldt River system that could easily make their way onto the IBA include exotic thistle, tamarisk, and cocklebur.

Less well-managed grazing on properties downstream is resulting in head-cutting in the river. This form of erosion tends to move upstream, resulting in entrenched stream channels and the separation of the stream from its floodplain. The resulting change in hydrology decreases the extent of wet meadow and riparian habitats and lowers the water table.

Mosquito spraying along the river corridor is likely affecting the prey base for insectivorous birds (and other wildlife, especially bats) in unknown ways. This issue has not been well studied here or elsewhere where mosquitoes are controlled by spraying.

Visiting the Site

The Boyd Humboldt Valley IBA lies entirely within private lands. However, the Boyd family welcomes bird watchers who have as much respect for their land as they do. If you visit this IBA *please* keep the following guidelines in mind: drive slowly, avoid the livestock, do not block roads when leaving vehicles to bird watch, don't block pasture gates, and perhaps most importantly, close gates when you find them closed. The last rule is particularly important on this ranch because of its proximity to the Union Pacific Railroad tracks. The trains don't slow down for bovines, or birders for that matter.

The IBA can be reached by taking Exit 317 off I-80 east of Elko. Follow the frontage road on the south side of the interstate as it angles south towards Elburz. Do not cross the railroad tracks at Elburz; instead, turn left (east) and follow the road parallel to the tracks. After a little less than half a mile, a farm access road crosses the tracks and enters the Boyd Ranch. Look for IBA signs along the way and at the gate. Note also that the bank between the road and railroad track between Elburz and the ranch entrance provides excellent views of the Humboldt River and wetlands. Make sure you pull off the road, and stay well clear of the railroad tracks.

Sandhill Cranes in flight

Carson Range

Area: 58,707 ha
UTM Easting: 249007
UTM Northing: 4349732

Description

The Carson Range is a spur of the Sierra Nevada and represents the entire occurrence of the Sierra Nevada ecoregion in the state of Nevada. Of the entire Carson Range, about 70 percent lies in Nevada and the remainder in California; this IBA addresses only the Nevada portion. The Sierra Meadows – Northern IBA, a complex of sites, lies adjacent to the Carson Range IBA in California (Cooper 2004) and includes portions of the Carson Range.

Wuerthner (1992) used the concept of island biogeography to explain the influence of the Sierra Nevada on the biodiversity of the state of Nevada. One of the tenants of biogeography states that the further one travels from the mainland source population, the fewer the number of species encountered. With this concept in mind, one can envision the Sierra Nevada on the west and the Rockies on the east as the "mainland" sources of plant and animal biodiversity, with decreasing biodiversity as one travels away from these cordilleras and towards the center of the Great Basin.

Biodiversity is indeed quite high in the Carson Range, with the most diverse tree and wildlife species encountered in Nevada (Wuerthner 1992). Tree species include lodgepole pine, western white pine, Jeffrey pine, incense cedar, mountain hemlock, red fir, sugar pine, and Washoe Pine (Wuerthner 1992). Most of the trees in the range are second growth, as the area was heavily logged to serve the fuel, building, and mining needs of Virginia City and other Comstock Era mining communities. A few isolated pockets of old growth forest remain, probably in steep drainages and in the few areas inaccessible to nineteenth century loggers.

In the context of the remainder of the state, the Carson Range is well watered. Some 60 inches of precipitation fall mostly as snow on the west side of Lake

Tahoe (in California), while the Nevada side of the lake receives about half that amount. There is also a steep rainfall gradient corresponding to elevation on the east slope of the Sierras. Rainfall at the foot of the east slope of the range can be as little as five inches. All of this variation in vegetation, rainfall, aspect, and to a lesser extent geology creates significant habitat and wildlife diversity.

A number of perennial streams and both the Carson and Truckee Rivers descend from the Carson Range. Wetlands associated with these systems are relatively restricted in extent, though certainly important to birds and avian diversity. Also of importance are the wet meadows which lie isolated in valleys and on benches where subsurface waters linger after snowmelt.

The list of land uses in the Carson Range IBA is lengthy. With much of the land under Forest Service management, land uses include most of the activities deemed appropriate under the Forest Service's multiple-use mandate: nature and wildlife conservation, wilderness, fishing, motorized and non-motorized recreation, research, watershed management for municipal water supply, and various types of forest management. Small and scattered portions of the IBA also include low density residential developments, though these areas are largely excluded from the IBA.

Birds

In considering the Carson Range IBA, two scales of evaluation are appropriate. In the context of Nevada, the site supports a unique avifaunal community associated with the Sierra Nevada. Species such as Pygmy Nuthatch, Band-tailed Pigeon, Mountain Quail, Pileated Woodpecker, White-headed Woodpecker, Black-backed Woodpecker, Red-breasted Sapsucker, and Winter Wren either occur nowhere else in the state or show up in far lower numbers in nearby ranges (the Winter Wren may breed in the Jarbidge Mountains IBA). All of these species hold far more extensive ranges in the California portion of the Sierra Nevada. However, Nevada does hold some responsibility for the stewardship of these species, and any conservation efforts on behalf of these species will by definition have to occur in the Carson Range.

Species used to identify the Carson Range IBA and the criteria met by the site. Proposed criteria are pending and will be evaluated by the National Technical Committee or the Nevada IBA TAC pending data availability. Proposed/confirmed codes are discussed in Appendices II and III.

Species	Year	Season	Min	Max	Units	Proposed	Confirmed
Cooper's Hawk	1998, 1999	breeding	--	600	pairs		NV1
Northern Goshawk	2000	breeding	--	--			NV1, NV2
White-headed Woodpecker	1997-1999	breeding	600	2,400	pairs	B1	NV1, NV2
Olive-sided Flycatcher	1997-2000	breeding	600	2,400	pairs	A1, NV3g	NV1, NV2
Willow Flycatcher	2003	breeding	2	10	pairs	NV3g	NV1, NV2
Western Bluebird	1998	breeding	--	600	pairs		NV1
MacGillivray's Warbler	1997-2000	breeding	--	2,500	pairs		NV1
Orange-crowned Warbler	1997-2000	staging	--	2,400	pairs		NV1, NV2

Many of the species that characterize the Carson Range are also Nevada Partners in Flight priority species, including Mountain Quail, Northern Goshawk, Cooper's Hawk, Flammulated Owl, Calliope Hummingbird, Lewis'

Woodpecker, Red-naped Sapsucker, White-headed Woodpecker, Olive-sided Flycatcher, Willow Flycatcher, Western Bluebird, Orange-crowned, MacGillivray's, and Wilson's Warblers, and Black Rosy-Finch are all Nevada Partners in Flight species of concern that rely on this landscape for various aspects of their life histories. The species of interest list broadens considerably if the Audubon Watch List, USFWS Species of Concern, and A1/B1 species list that drives the selection of global and continental IBAs are all consulted.

Conservation Issues

Because this landscape is so large and experiences a gamut of uses, threats identified for this IBA are also diverse and vary in intensity depending on location. Catastrophic fire is a possibility every fire season, and in 2004 a large portion of the IBA west of Carson City burned dramatically in the Waterfall Fire. The urban-wildland interface and the close proximity of people adds to the threat of natural fires initiated by lightening strikes. The Waterfall Fire was apparently caused by an unattended campfire. In addition to the direct loss of habitat, such fires in steep terrain also create erosion concerns, and at lower elevations there is the added risk of invasive plant species. In the Lake Tahoe Basin, fire management efforts, including fuels reduction programs, are ongoing. While the concerns driving these actions are well founded (private property protection, water quality concerns for Lake Tahoe, view shed protection), management actions must incorporate maintaining wildlife values in the treated stands.

Development in this landscape is a minor concern but warrants monitoring. Most of the landscape is in public lands, either Nevada State Parks or Forest Service, and thus development opportunities are limited. However, in-holdings and private lands do occur in the area and development of these areas could increase fragmentation in the landscape.

Visiting the Site

Much of the Carson Range IBA is managed by the Humboldt-Toiyabe National Forest, and a significant portion by Nevada State Parks. Favorite locations for bird and wildlife watchers include Spooner Lake State Park, Lake Tahoe State Park, and Tahoe Meadows. Numerous trails crisscross the IBA, most noteworthy of which is the Tahoe Rim Trail.

White-headed Woodpecker (© Bob Goodman)

34

Carson River Delta

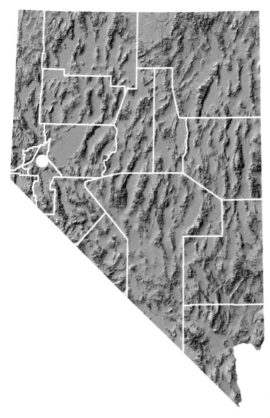

Area: 2,468 ha
UTM Easting: 311036
UTM Northing: 4353309

Description

The Carson River Delta IBA was recognized largely for its habitat values; the site constitutes the last best remnant of a cottonwood-willow riparian forest in northwestern Nevada (and perhaps an even larger area). This habitat type was once extensive along perennial water courses in Nevada, including the Truckee and Carson Rivers. These forests suffered as they were cut for fuel, grazed, and eliminated as rivers were diverted or dammed, and simply clearcut under the misguided notion that removing riparian forests would increase stream flows.

In spite of these problems, the Carson River Delta IBA is spectacular to the eye, and appears as a dense, verdant forest spread along the historic flood plain. The scene is striking against the starkness of the surrounding desert shrub communities and barren rock outcrops on adjacent hillsides. The IBA encompasses the historic flood plain of the Carson River from Fort Churchill downstream to the river's delta at the Lahontan Reservoir. In high runoff years the river leaves its banks and floods the forest in spring. In sharp contrast, above-ground flow in this stretch of the Carson River often vanishes in early July and does not resume again until mid-to-late October.

Land uses in the Carson River Delta IBA include hunting, conservation and research, tourism and recreation, and water management. Land use on the Fort Churchill portion of the site also includes cattle ranching; the state park issues a five year grazing lease that includes grazing rights to the river corridor.

Birds

Riparian forests have been severely impacted in Nevada and throughout much of the West. As a result, many of the bird species dependent on this habitat type have also experienced dramatic declines in numbers. Both Yellow-billed

Cuckoos and Willow Flycatchers, two species whose ranges have shrunk dramatically from historic levels (Hughes 1999, Sedgewick 2000), have been recorded in recent years on the Carson River Delta IBA. Other Nevada Partners In Flight species of concern found at this site include White-faced Ibis, Swainson's Hawk, Western Bluebird, and Wilson's Warbler. The riparian forest is an important migration corridor, providing stopover habitat for Neotropical migrants. To increase our understanding of the bird community on this IBA, point count surveys were initiated in 2002 and a banding station was established in the same year using Monitoring Avian Productivity and Survivorship (MAPS) protocol.

Species used to identify the Carson River Delta IBA and the criteria met by the site. Confirmed codes are discussed in Appendix II.

Species	Year	Season	Min	Max	Units	Confirmed
Bald Eagle	2002	breeding	-	2	adults	NV1
Cooper's Hawk	2001	breeding	2	10	adults	NV1
Yellow-billed Cuckoo	1997	breeding	1	2	adults	NV1, NV2
Willow Flycatcher	2002	breeding	3	-	individuals	NV1, NV2
Western Bluebird	2002	migration	40	-	individuals	NV1

Conservation Issues

Invasive weeds are a serious problem throughout most of the lower Carson River watershed. Species of particular concern include tall whitetop and tamarisk. Both of these species can form dense, monotypic stands that out-compete other plants and severely degrade habitat. Lahontan State Recreation Area recently initiated significant control efforts, and coordinated, systemic (i.e., watershed-wide) control efforts are also needed on the Carson River.

Cottonwood regeneration is tightly linked to natural flood cycles, with the release of cottonwood seeds timed to take advantage of receding spring floods. As rivers have been dammed and diverted, these events rarely occur at all. Efforts to manage the river to at least simulate historic flow patterns to encourage cottonwood restoration are needed.

Cattle grazing and associated land management practices have altered the habitat, most notably in the western portion of the IBA. Ongoing grazing is suppressing forest regeneration and reducing willow cover along water channels. Fort Churchill State Park leases grazing rights on large portions of its property and manages these lands to benefit grazing. Stakeholders should facilitate the park's transition from a ranching-based economy to a more

Spring canoeing in the Carson River Delta IBA

Carson River

sustainable recreation based economy. The wild horse herd in the area also impacts vegetation through concentrated grazing and trampling. The herd was reduced from about 250 head to about 10 animals in 2004 in response to concerns about the horses' impact on the riparian habitat.

As a result of mercury contamination from historic mining activity, the Carson River below Dayton is Nevada's only Superfund site (U.S. Environmental Protection Agency 2005). Cleanup costs would be massive and would also result in severe habitat disturbance. Mercury accumulation in birds seems to occur primarily in the Lahontan Reservoir and studies of the effects of mercury on fish and birds are ongoing.

Finally, portions of the IBA are periodically sprayed for mosquito control purposes. The impacts of this activity on the bird community on the Carson River Delta IBA are unknown, but could include a reduction in the forage base for insectivorous birds.

Visiting the Site

Managed under the Nevada State Parks system, the Carson River Delta IBA is an excellent destination for wildlife watchers. In spring (approximately May - early July) canoeing the Carson River is an excellent way to experience the area. Put in at the Fort Churchill State Park picnic area and take out at the end of Ninth St. in Silver Springs. Another alternative is to explore the area on foot. There is a walking trail on the south side of the river opposite Buckland Station, near Fort Churchill. Whether you explore by foot or boat, check with Fort Churchill State Park for current conditions and specific access points.

Fort Churchill State Park lies along US Alt 95, about eight miles south of the intersection of US 95 and US 50 in Silver Springs. Lahontan State Recreation Area, is about 10 miles east of the US 95/50 intersection in Silver Springs, on US 50.

Carson Valley

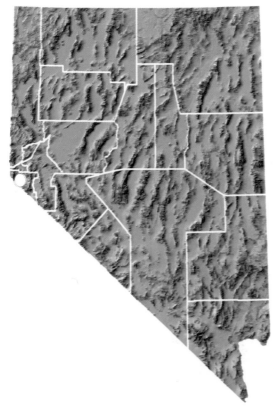

Area: 18,818 ha
UTM Easting: 257970
UTM Northing: 4320031

Description

On the western side of the Carson Valley, pasture, grasslands, riparian wetlands, and the Carson River corridor comprise the Carson Valley IBA.

Few well-watered valleys drain the eastern slope of the Sierra Nevada, and with ever-increasing development these few valleys are growing ever-smaller in the extent of habitat they offer wildlife. The irrigated pasture and hay meadows supported in part by distributed irrigation offer habitat for a variety of birds. Raptors are abundant in the valley, particularly in winter, and there is a growing population of Bald Eagles that is taking advantage of the calf birthing season that is timed to peak in February.

Land use in the Carson Valley IBA is in transition from agricultural to low density residential development. Some hunting still occurs, primarily for waterfowl. The valley is a popular destination for tourism and recreation.

Birds

The Carson Valley has one of the few colonies of Tri-colored Blackbirds outside of California and the only colony in Nevada. Sandhill Cranes also bred in the valley for the past several years, a rare occurrence though they probably occurred in the valley historically. The valley supports numerous Nevada Partners in Flight priority conservation species, and an abundance of over-wintering raptors, including Bald Eagle, Golden Eagle, Red-tailed Hawk, Ferruginous Hawk, Rough-legged Hawk, Northern Harrier, Cooper's Hawk, Sharp-shinned Hawk, Prairie Falcon, American Kestrel, Peregrine Falcon, Merlin (a few), Swainson's Hawk and Osprey (summer), Barn Owl, Great-horned Owl, Long-eared Owl, Short-eared Owl, Northern Pygmy Owl, and Flammulated Owl. The raptors provide essential pest control and occupy every niche–from wetland associated species to birds characteristic of the drier uplands.

The Carson River corridor was probably an important songbird migration route prior to the reduction in willow-cottonwood forests. The valley's wetlands are home to a diversity of waterbirds, from rails to ducks to herons and egrets and Red-winged Blackbirds. Many species of shorebird stopover in the valley during migration.

Other birds of the open grasslands include Short-eared Owls, White-faced Ibis, and Sandhill Cranes. The latter is present in very modest numbers but could grow if adequate habitat is maintained.

Species used to identify the Carson Valley IBA and the criteria met by the site. Proposed Criteria are pending and will be evaluated by the National Technical Committee or the Nevada IBA TAC pending data availability. Proposed/confirmed codes are discussed in Appendices II and III.

Species	Year	Season	Min	Max	Units	Proposed	Confirmed
White-faced Ibis	2001	breeding	200	400	individuals		NV1
Bald Eagle	2003	winter	0	31	individuals		NV1, NV3g, NV3d
Northern Harrier	2002	winter	15	25	individuals		NV3d
Red-tailed Hawk	2003	winter	50	150	individuals		NV3d
Ferruginous Hawk	2002	winter	3	6	individuals	NV1	NV3d
Rough-legged Hawk	2003	winter	10	15	individuals		NV3d
American Kestrel	2002	winter	15	20	individuals		NV3d
Bank Swallow	2001	breeding	200	300	adults only	NV3g	NV1
Tricolored Blackbird	2001	breeding	100	150	adults only	B1	NV3g

The Carson River on its passage through the Carson Valley

Conservation Issues

The Carson Valley is probably the second most threatened IBA in Nevada after Walker Lake IBA. The primary threat to this landscape is conversion through development. Ranchers in the valley find themselves in the possession of expensive and coveted land that pays far more for a crop of houses than cattle. At the end of careers many find themselves without heirs interested in taking over their ranching operation, and with most of their financial assets in land. Under the circumstances, ranches are sold, subdivided, and developed. Some areas in the valley have a minimum lot size of 20 acres. While this practice reduces housing density, it does not provide habitat for Sandhill Cranes and species that are similarly intolerant of human disturbance.

The quality of the habitat along the Carson River has been compromised over a century-and-a-half of settlement. Vegetation has been altered and in the case of cottonwoods removed from long stretches. Grazing is one of the practices that has altered vegetation and river geomorphology, preceded by log drives during the Comstock Era that must have devastated the river and its floodplain. Efforts are being made to recover the riparian vegetation along the river, and reaches where work has occurred appear to be on their way to rebounding.

Weeds are a potential issue in this landscape, but they do not appear to constitute an imminent threat. Because of the long history of agriculture and settlement, an example of probably every weed in the western part of the state can be found here—tamarisk, canary reed grass, tall whitetop, sticky gum weed, and so on. This situation warrants monitoring and management on a site-by-site basis.

Visiting the Site

A significant portion of this IBA lies on private lands. However, wildlife viewing from roadsides can be rewarding. Raptor watching is popular in winter and human activities peak in February with the influx of Bald Eagles and the annual Eagles and Agriculture Tour.

Burrowing Owl (© Bob Goodman)

Catclaw Washes

Area: 2,261 ha
UTM Easting: 701148
UTM Northing: 3914022

Description

This site consists of a complex of several catclaw acacia washes that run down Piute Valley (primarily west of US 95) and along the crest and eastern flanks of the Newberry Mountains. Specifically, the washes included are Hiko Wash and Springs, Piute, Roman, Sacatone, and Grapevine Washes. Sacatone and Grapevine Washes are within Lake Mead National Recreation Area, while the remaining washes are managed by the BLM.

These washes rarely sustain surface flows except in times of flash floods and for short stretches below perennial springs. However, wash vegetation is distinctly different from adjacent uplands and is characterized by more mesic species than those encountered in immediately adjacent uplands. The latter tend to offer creosote bush and various species of yucca. The washes support catclaw acacia, mesquite, cottonwood, desert willow, and sandbar willow. These species are indicative of ground water resources that are within reach of plant roots.

Land uses in the catclaw washes range from nature and wildlife conservation to hunting, various forms of recreation, research, and utility corridors.

Birds

The unique vegetation of the washes supports a suite of bird species that is distinct from the surrounding desert, although it should be noted that birds from the desert uplands may also utilize these areas. The washes were nominated and recognized for the critical resources they offer to Phainopepla, a species of concern in Nevada. Phainopepla rely heavily on the mistletoe seed crop produced in these areas. The mistletoe in turn is dependent on the catclaw acacia and mesquite as hosts. The Phainopepla also nest in the acacia and mesquite.

The densities of Phainopeplas at this site are consistently among the highest in the state (only two other sites have comparable densities), and in some years breeding success in Piute Valley is higher than anywhere else known. Moreover, the milder temperatures at this complex of sites may help Phainopeplas persist when they cannot occupy other sites in the state (subfreezing temperatures cause mistletoe berries to freeze, leaving the birds nothing to eat).

Many other species of concern in southern Nevada utilize the tall shrubs and trees found in these washes. Several washes (especially Piute) are many kilometers long and likely provide migration corridors. Birds utilizing these washes as stopover sites for migration gain opportunities for foraging, resting, and accessing surface water where it is available.

Species used to identify the Catclaw Washes IBA and the criteria met by the site. Confirmed codes are discussed in Appendix II.

| Species | Year | Season | birds/km | | Units | Confirmed |
			Min	Max		
Phainopepla - Hiko	00-02	all	-	60	individuals	NV1, NV2
Phainopepla - Hiko	93-99	winter	-	30	individuals	NV1, NV2
Phainopepla - Roman	00-02	all	-	46	individuals	NV1, NV2
Phainopepla - Grapevine/Sacatone	00-02	all	-	32	individuals	NV1, NV2
Phainopepla - Piute	00-02	all	-	72	individuals	NV1, NV2
Ash-throated Flycatcher	01-02	migration	-	4	individuals	NV1

Conservation Issues

Phainopeplas in Nevada occur in the mesquite and catclaw acacia habitat of Clark County and southern Nye and Lincoln counties, the northern edge of their breeding and over-wintering desert range. This habitat type is threatened both directly and indirectly by economic development in Clark County, and by mesquite collectors.

The Southern Nevada Water Authority (SNWA) is seeking water to quench the ever-increasing thirst of Las Vegas, and groundwater pumping is the primary mechanism for meeting this need. At the moment SNWA seems focused on areas to the north of Las Vegas, but there is fear that groundwater pumping in the aquifers underlying the Catclaw Washes could occur and would lead to a drop in the water table and the subsequent decline of the plants that characterize the washes.

ORV use is largely unregulated or poorly policed in the washes although it is specifically prohibited. In some thus-far limited areas, this activity has encouraged erosion, disturbed birds, caused the loss of native vegetation, and facilitated the spread of weeds.

In 2002, catastrophic breeding failure of Phainopepla in Roman and Piute Washes occurred due to nest predation, probably by ravens using nearby power lines as hunting perches. Susceptibility of the Phainopepla nests is believed to have been exacerbated by prolonged drought. Small mammals and herpetofauna may also have contributed to nest losses. Tamarisk has made incursions into some of the washes, particularly Grapevine Wash. Although conditions seem to

Grapevine Canyon has long attracted wildlife and human visitors

be less than ideal for its establishment, without treatment it will eventually dominate the system.

Visiting the Site

The Catclaw Washes vary in their accessibility. The best spots for bird watching opportunities are likely to be Grapevine Wash and Sacatone Wash, both located off Christmas Tree Pass Road, off of NV 163 and about five miles west of Laughlin. Both of these washes have parking areas (at their lower or east ends) and well worn trails. Spring is the best time to visit, with the mix of local breeding birds and migrants maximizing local diversity.

David E. Moore Bird and Wildlife Sanctuary

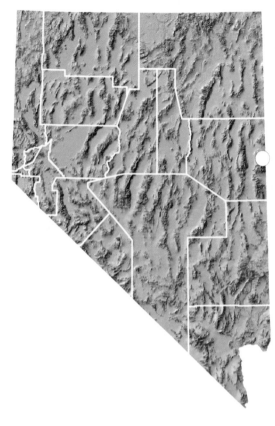

Area: 259 ha
UTM Easting: 744331
UTM Northing: 4321872

Description

The sanctuary lies in a transition zone where the piñon-juniper forests of the Great Basin foothills meet the desert shrub community. Two perennial streams converge on the site, providing wet meadows and permanent surface water where livestock was once confined. The sanctuary is on the site of the historic Circle M Ranch, and the land is recovering from decades of grazing and other domestic uses. The site lies along the entrance road to Great Basin National Park IBA and as such provides a valuable outreach opportunity. True to its name, the site is set aside specifically for nature conservation.

Birds

As an ecotone, the site provides a rich, mixed bird community characteristic of transitional zones. Most noteworthy is a population of Long-billed Curlews. The Greater Sage-Grouse was once common here, but the local population dwindled and now appears to have disappeared all together (D. Moore, pers. comm.). Pinyon Jays are a common sight at this IBA, though their occurrence here is transitory as they move about the larger landscape.

Conservation Issues

Because the Moore Sanctuary was established to protect wildlife, the future of the area is largely secured for birds. However, active management will be required to protect the area from extrinsic factors like invasive plants, and to manage visitors. A recently initiated project with many contributing partners has been kicked off in an effort to restore and enhance habitat quality at the site, with the ultimate goal of restoring Greater Sage-Grouse to the sanctuary.

Species used to identify the D.E. Moore Sanctuary IBA and the criteria met by the site. Criteria codes are discussed in Appendix II.						
Species	Year	Season	Min	Max	Units	Confirmed
Pinyon Jay	2001	all	0	500	individuals	NV1
Long-billed Curlew	2003	breeding	4	12	individuals	NV1

Visiting the Site

Visitors are welcome to stroll around the Moore Sanctuary. A pullout and parking area is located on the south side of NV 488 between Baker and the entrance to Great Basin National Park. Look for the Moore Sanctuary signs as well as IBA signs posted along the fence line.

Wet meadows at the D. E. Moore IBA

Franklin Lake

Area: 4,987 ha
UTM Easting: 637552
UTM Northing: 4472248

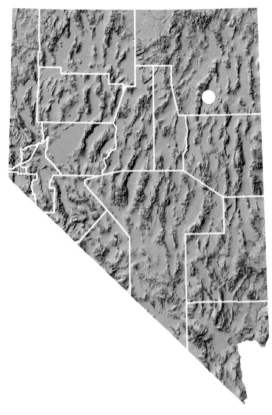

Description

Franklin Lake presents one of the true paradoxes of the Great Basin Desert. In wet years the site veritably teams with waterbirds in an abundance so great that the mind boggles. In dry years the site is a pasture which often has more cattle than birds of all species combined. The dry years far exceed the wet, and the more common experience involves standing at the visitor's parking area and scratching your head, feeling certain you've been duped in the best tradition of a greenhorn prospector by reports of hundreds of thousands of birds. But this is the typical pattern of the desert—the wild ride from lavish abundance to bewildering impoverishment.

The site is a mixture of land ownership and management, including interests held by the Nevada Department of Wildlife, BLM, and some private parcels. Franklin Lake is a seasonal wetland-playa fed by the Franklin River. The size of the marshes vary according to available runoff. The lake is about five miles north of Ruby Lake NWR IBA. In wet years birds move between Franklin Lake and Ruby Lake NWR. The Nature Conservancy holds easements on state lands and one of four private ranches.

Land uses at Franklin Lake include rangeland (in dry years), hunting, conservation, research, and wildlife viewing.

Birds

Franklin Lake hosts an extraordinary abundance—tens of thousands—of waterbirds in wet years. Forster's, Caspian, and Black Terns use the wetland as foraging and breeding habitat. Greater Sage-Grouse occur on the upland portion of the system. Sage Sparrows are a common breeding species. A few Bald Eagles winter here. There is a small, non-migratory experimental population of Trumpeter Swans associated primarily with Ruby Lake NWR that utilizes the area in wet years.

Species used to identify the Franklin Lake IBA and the criteria met by the site. Proposed criteria will be evaluated with the availability of more data on statewide bird populations. Codes for criteria are discussed in Appendix II.

Species	Year	Season	Min	Max	Units	Proposed	Confirmed
White-faced Ibis	1998	breeding	--	300	adults only	NV3g	NV1, NV2, NV3e
Ruddy Duck	1997	migration	--	235	individuals		NV3a
Canada Goose	1997	migration	--	505	individuals		NV3a
Gadwall	1997	migration	--	5,209	individuals		NV3g
American Wigeon	1997	migration	--	1,136	individuals		NV3a
Mallard	1997	migration	--	8,572	individuals		NV3a
Cinnamon Teal	1997	migration	--	3,717	individuals		NV3a
Northern Shoveler	1997	migration	--	4,624	individuals	NV3g	NV3a
Northern Pintail	1997	migration	--	10,507	individuals	NV3g	NV3a
Green-winged Teal	1997	migration	--	16,316	individuals	NV3g	NV3a
Canvasback	1997	migration	--	1,005	individuals		NV3g,NV3a
Redhead	1997	migration	--	2,403	individuals	NV3g	NV3a
Sandhill Crane	1998	migration	--	400	individuals	NV3g	NV1, NV3e
American Coot	1997	migration	--	3,676	individuals		NV3a
American Avocet	1998	migration	--	1,000	individuals	NV3g	NV1, NV2, NV3e

Conservation Issues

The primary constraint on Franklin Lake and its habitat quality is the availability of water. The system is at nature's mercy and awaits years of high snow pack and runoff from the adjacent Ruby Mountains.

Visiting the Site

Public access to Franklin Lake is provided along Ruby Valley Road, just north of Ruby Wash Road and the Ruby Lake NWR. The turnoff is signed and the short road ends at a turnaround that overlooks the lowlands of Franklin Lake. If a visit to the site proves to be a bust, Ruby Lake NWR is a short drive to the south and is always worth a visit.

Franklin Lake (© Bob Goodman)

Goshute Mountains

Area: 58,031 ha
UTM Easting: 730363
UTM Northing: 4499025

Description

The Goshute Mountains form a 100-km long ridge that runs north-south and just west of the Utah-Nevada border. The higher elevations of the ridge line are encompassed by the Goshute Wilderness Study Area. The heart of the range is approximately 40 km southwest of Wendover, Nevada, and the entire site is on land administered by the BLM, Elko District. Forests of white fir, limber pine, bristlecone pine, piñon, and juniper flank the slopes at higher elevations (Wuerthner 1992), grading into grasslands and shrublands at lower elevations. Mountain mahogany is a prominent shrub, especially on exposed portions of the ridge.

It is not so much the vegetation as it is the land form and location that make the Goshutes unique. Most ranges in the Great Basin probably support raptor migrations in the fall and spring. But the Goshutes are uniquely positioned to act as the narrow mouth of a funnel, with numerous mountain ranges to the north angling into the north end of the Goshutes and concentrating raptors in this corridor. HawkWatch International has been conducting annual migration counts in the Goshutes since the early 1980s.

Land uses in the Goshute Mountains include conservation and research, tourism and recreation in an undeveloped setting, hunting, and rangeland, though grazing allotments are primarily at lower elevations on the range. It is worth pointing out that the Goshutes have the longest unbroken history of any site in Nevada as a location for avian research.

Birds

Among the myriad mountain ranges in Nevada, geographic and physiographic factors converge to make the Goshute Mountains unique in the state. For migrating raptors, the Great Salt Lake Desert is an inhospitable barrier to the

Ferruginous Hawk (© Bob Goodman)

east of the Goshute Range. The desert lacks prey, roost habitat, and the orographic lift of air masses that saves migrating raptors critical energy. Mountain ranges to the north of the Goshutes (Black Pine, Raft River, Grouse Creek, Pilot, and Toana Mountains) tend to angle towards the north end of the range like an ever tightening funnel, thus focusing columns of raptors moving southward. These conditions are responsible for the Goshute flyway offering one of the largest known concentrations of migrant raptors in western North America with as many as 20,000 individuals passing in a peak season (Smith and Vekasy 2001). HawkWatch International has expanded migration monitoring efforts at this site to investigate owls.

Three species have been trapped and banded through these efforts, with a noteworthy population of owls documented using this migration corridor.

Species used to identify the Goshute Mountains IBA and the criteria met by the site. Data from Smith and Vekasy (2001) and Smith (2005). Proposed criteria await evaluation by the National Technical Committee (B1) or await additional data for the Nevada IBA TAC. Codes are discussed in Appendices II and III.

Species	Year	Season	Min	Max	Units	Proposed	Confirmed
Northern Harrier	1999	migration	-	356	individuals	B1, NV3g	NV3d, NV4
Sharp-shinned Hawk	1998	migration	-	9,598	individuals	NV3g	NV3d, NV4
Cooper's Hawk	1998	migration	-	6,736	individuals	NV3g	NV1, NV3d, NV4
Northern Goshawk	1992	migration	-	259	individuals		NV1, NV3g, NV3d, NV4
Broad-winged Hawk	1998	migration	-	160	individuals		NV3g, NV3d, NV4
Swainson's Hawk	1998	migration	-	507	individuals	B1, NV3g	NV1, NV3d, NV4
Red-tailed Hawk	1999	migration	-	5,183	individuals	NV3g	NV3d, NV4
Golden Eagle	1999	migration	-	348	individuals	NV3g	NV3d, NV4
Osprey	1997	migration	-	187	individuals	NV3g	NV3d, NV4
American Kestrel	1997	migration	-	3,394	individuals	NV3g	NV3d, NV4
Merlin	1998	migration	-	91	individuals	NV3g	NV3d, NV4
Flammulated Owl	2003	migration	-	26	individuals		NV1, NV4

Conservation Issues

The site's management agency, the BLM, is well aware of the value of this site to migrating raptors. As such, management favors efforts to preserve the values of the site for migrating raptors. There has been some concern expressed about trespass grazing or a potential increase in permitted grazing, though threats from these sources are low at this time. This region of Nevada seems particularly vulnerable to large-scale habitat conversion as a result of fires. This is always a looming possibility and, if a fire occurred, efforts to reseed and quickly rehabilitate the affected part of the range would be warranted.

Visiting the Site

A visit to the Goshute Mountains can be a lifetime experience. The best time to visit is when HawkWatch International is counting raptors in the fall (August 15 – November 5). The organization has an educator on site to interpret the count effort and assist visitors with the location and identification of raptors.

To reach the best raptor viewing area, travel south from Wendover on US Alt 93 to the NDOT station at Ferguson Springs. Turn west past the station and follow the gravel road 4.2 miles to the parking area at the trailhead. From here, the ridge and viewing site are a 2.5-mile vigorous hike. Bring plenty of water and any supplies to be self sufficient (e.g., food) as HawkWatch has supplies on hand only for their staff. Maps and current site information are available at HawkWatch International's web site, http://www.hawkwatch.org.

Sunrise on the east slope of the Goshute Mountains

Great Basin National Park

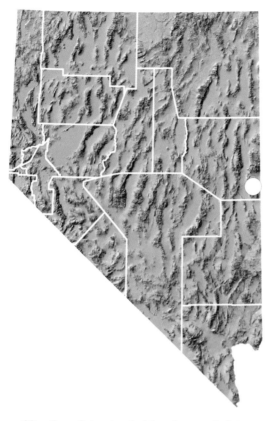

Area: 31,173 ha
UTM Easting: 737712
UTM Northing: 4314196

Description

Great Basin National Park encompasses the southern end of the Snake Range in east-central Nevada. It is bordered by broad valleys, on the east by Snake Valley and on the west by Spring Valley. The most prominent feature is Wheeler Peak at 13,063 ft., the second highest point in Nevada. Influenced by the broad elevation range and topographic relief, vegetation zones from salt desert scrub to an alpine zone create a diversity of habitats, including five of the seven Merriam's life zones described for North America. Nine perennial streams flow from the park and support over 30 miles of riparian habitat from subalpine meadows to aspen, cottonwood, and dense shrub thickets. Land uses in this IBA include conservation, research, fishing, hiking, camping, auto touring, caving, wildlife viewing, and designated wilderness.

Birds

Numerous avid birders have surveyed Nevada's high country for bird species endemic to alpine and subalpine habitats. Although the habitats can be found on the summit of several of the state's 314 ranges, the characteristic birds are for the most part absent. In contrast, this IBA has both the alpine and sub-alpine habitats and the bird species associated with them.

Of the 51 birds listed in the Nevada Partners in Flight priority list, 28 have ranges that encompass Great Basin National Park. Another five species have range distributions that are adjacent to Great Basin National Park. Several Nevada Partners in Flight priority species are found in significant densities here. These species include Black-throated Gray Warbler, Red-naped Sapsucker, MacGillivray's Warbler, Wilson's Warbler, Pinyon Jay, and Yellow-breasted Chat.

Most of the sensitive birds documented for Great Basin National Park are Neotropical migrants and tend to use riparian areas for breeding. Point count data in riparian areas have detected numerous Black-throated Gray Warblers, MacGillivray's Warbler, Wilson's Warbler, Yellow-breasted Chat, and Red-naped Sapsucker.

Medin (1982) found the greatest diversity of birds in mountain big sagebrush, mountain big sagebrush-steppe, and mixed conifer habitats. Priority species found in this habitat type include Greater Sage-Grouse, Sage Sparrow, Sage Thrasher, Vesper Sparrow, Virginia's Warbler, Orange-crowned Warbler, MacGillivray's Warbler, Olive-sided Flycatcher, and Calliope Hummingbird.

The high elevation alpine, subalpine, and spruce forests within Great Basin National Park are relatively intact habitats despite some historic logging and grazing activities. The history of wildfires in these habitats indicates that they are within the natural range of variation. Birds from the Nevada Partners in Flight priority list include Black Rosy-Finch, Three-toed Woodpecker, Olive-sided Flycatcher, Calliope Hummingbird, Prairie Falcon, and Northern Goshawk.

Quantitative surveys for raptors have not occurred at Great Basin National Park. However, all raptors listed in the Nevada Partners in Flight priority list have been documented in and around Great Basin National Park. It is possible that the southern Snake Range provides a corridor for migratory raptors but this has not been confirmed. The high elevation and nearly continuous winds provide optimal conditions for soaring and elevation gain. Cliff faces and late successional conifer stands and deciduous riparian habitats with large trees and snags provide widespread raptor nesting habitat.

Species used to identify the Great Basin National Park IBA and the criteria met by the site. Proposed Criteria are pending the availability of additional data on species' abundance in Nevada. Criteria codes are discussed in Appendix II.

Species	Year	Season	Min	Max	Units	Proposed	Confirmed
Northern Goshawk	1982	breeding	19	117	individuals		NV1, NV2
Calliope Hummingbird	1982	breeding	200	625	individuals	NV3g	NV1
Olive-sided Flycatcher	1996	breeding	150	312	individuals	NV3g	NV1, NV2
Sage Sparrow	1982	breeding	687	2,030	individuals		NV1
Virginia's Warbler	1997	breeding	0	937	individuals	NV3g	NV1
Black-throated Gray Warbler	1998	breeding	0	1,249	individuals		NV1
MacGillivray's Warbler	1999	breeding	625	1,874	individuals	NV3g	NV1
Black Rosy-Finch	1982	breeding	20	195	individuals		NV1, NV2, NV3g
Pinyon Jay	1996	breeding	1,749	6,997	individuals	NV3g	NV1

Conservation Issues

Great Basin National Park is a site that is certain to maintain, restore, and perpetuate Great Basin habitats required by over half of the Nevada Partners in Flight priority birds. National Park status ensures protection of these habitats and increased promotion of conservation within and adjacent to the park.

There are two primary conservation issues. One is the expansion of the piñon-juniper and mountain mahogany types with subsequent closure of the canopy in savannah and shrub-steppe habitats. The second concern is the effect of groundwater pumping on springs and stream discharge.

Long-term livestock grazing and fire suppression have encouraged piñon-juniper and mountain mahogany expansion and canopy closure. Livestock grazing over the past 100 years removed fine fuels that allowed slow, cool burns across the landscape, limiting tree canopy closure and expansion. Time intervals between fires have increased and facilitated increasing tree density and expansion beyond historic distributions. Modern human fire suppression exacerbated this effect by further lengthening the time interval between fires. The result is significant loss of shrub-steppe habitats and altered fire cycles that may foster higher intensity fires that will impede recovery of the sites to shrub-steppe.

Though some 20,000 acres of sagebrush-steppe and savannah still exist within Great Basin National Park, over 12,000 acres have succeeded to dense piñon-juniper and mahogany woodlands, resulting in smaller fragmented patches of sagebrush-steppe. Great Basin National Park has initiated mechanical thinning projects to reduce canopy cover and to encourage shrub-steppe vegetation to return. The park will be able to reintroduce fire without fear of large-scale, high-intensity events.

The second concern of groundwater pumping involves the Southern Nevada Water Authority, Lincoln County, and lobbyist and developer Harvey Whittemore. These three parties have applied for and own extensive water rights in the vicinity of Great Basin National Park. The concern is that the use

of these rights via groundwater pumping could eliminate springs and reduce stream flows in the park, subsequently reducing riparian habitats. The park is pursuing research and monitoring to determine what impacts could occur with groundwater pumping.

Visiting the Site

Great Basin National Park welcomes visitors and provides numerous opportunities for wildlife viewing and bird watching. The park entrance is located just west of Baker on NV 488. The visitors' center at the Park offers a bird checklist and information about birding opportunities. Some of the highlights include the Bristlecone Pine Trail and Snake Creek. Some of the park campgrounds are great places for casual birding.

Mount Wheeler (© Bob Goodman)

Gridley Lake

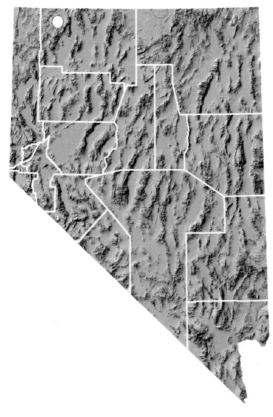

Area: 114 ha
UTM Easting: 346119
UTM Northing: 4623588

Description

Gridley Lake lies in the low desert east of Sheldon NWR and southwest of the small community of Denio. Many playa lakes dot the landscape across northeastern Nevada, but Gridley Lake appears to be unique because it has a permanent water source.

The lake is ephemeral and its most consistent features are an alkali playa and a permanent sheen of spring-fed water along the northeastern edge. The extent of the alkali playa and the shallow lake vary according to rainfall and runoff. The permanent water supports brine flies and brine shrimp, an important food source for birds that can tolerate the harsh environment. Management responsibility for the area lies with the BLM. The entire site is a wetland and is utilized as wildlife habitat.

Birds

Gridley Lake is a remote and little visited alkali playa offering permanent water and food to bird species tolerant of these extreme conditions. The harsh environment does not support high species diversity, but breeding by American Avocet and Killdeer has been consistently documented. Additional species and numbers are likely in migration, though documentation is needed. The site is most noteworthy for having one of the highest breeding populations of Snowy Plover in Nevada.

Species used to identify Gridley Lake IBA and the criteria met by the site. Proposed Criteria await evaluation by the National Technical Committee. Criteria codes are discussed in Appendices II and III.

Species	Year	Season	Min	Max	Units	Proposed	Confirmed
Snowy Plover	2002	breeding	--	72	individuals	B1	NV1, NV2, NV3g

Conservation Issues

Water rights have been claimed and allotted on the springs that provide the permanent surface water to Gridley Lake and sustain nesting birds each year. At the time of this writing the water was going primarily to Gridley Lake, though it is possible in the future that water users could choose to divert water for agricultural purposes. Because of the nature of Nevada water rights laws it is difficult to secure and hold water for wildlife.

Wild burros, which are not native to Nevada, appear to be the primary users of the springs and range lands immediately surrounding Gridley Lake. The lake is fenced, so the burros and other livestock are excluded from sensitive habitats where birds nest. However, maintenance of this fence, particularly through nesting season, will be critical to the integrity of the site.

Visiting the Site

Though quite remote, this site is well worth a visit if you happen to be passing by, perhaps traveling between Denio and Gerlach. Gridley Lake is immediately adjacent to the gravel road connecting these two areas, and the area is just outside the eastern boundary of Sheldon NWR. Once the playa is located, it is possible to pull off the road and scan the entire area with binoculars or a spotting scope.

Gridley Lake and playa

High Rock Resource Area

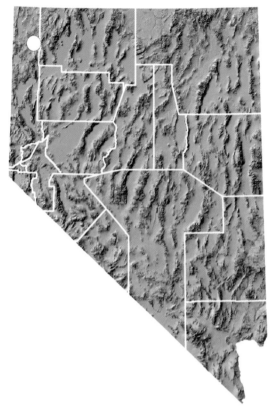

Area: 151,436 ha
UTM Easting: 291485
UTM Northing: 4580794

Description

The Columbia Plateau region of northern Nevada is remote and nearly unpopulated, featuring rolling, sagebrush-covered terrain divided by rugged canyons that reveal the underlying lava flows which define the landscape. This site is defined by the juxtaposition of two resources, cliffs and water. High Rock Canyon is a rugged, steep defile that shelters at least five species of nesting raptors (Clark 1993) and a large concentration of Cliff and Violet-green Swallows (Clark 1993, Nevada Wilderness 2002). Desert shrub communities along with adjacent riparian thickets and perennial water in the canyon floor increase habitat complexity and species diversity. On the eastern edge of this area, ephemeral High Rock Lake supports spring migrant waterfowl and shorebirds (Clark 1993) in years with adequate precipitation.

The High Rock Resource Area supports one of the three largest Greater Sage-Grouse populations in Nevada (S. Stiver, Nevada Department of Wildlife, pers. comm.). Visits to the area in 2003 revealed the habitat to be in good condition with only isolated pockets of excessive grazing and little evidence of weeds. The High Rock Resource Area IBA contains portions of the East Fork High Rock Canyon High Rock Canyon, Little High Rock Canyon, and High Rock Lake wilderness areas. These areas include cliff habitats and isolated springs in addition to those located in High Rock Canyon. Land uses in the IBA include nature conservation, designated wilderness, rangeland (in the form of leased grazing allotments), and tourism and recreation.

Birds

The area provides cliff nesting sites in association with relatively abundant water and food resources, which support a high density of species dependent on cliff habitats for nesting or for some portion of their life history. In addition, the area sustains one of the best Greater Sage-Grouse populations in the state. Noteworthy cliff nesting species include Violet-green and Cliff Swallows, Canyon Wren, Prairie Falcon, Red-tailed Hawk, Golden Eagle, and American Kestrel (Clark 1993).

Species used to identify the High Rock Resource Area IBA and the criteria met by the site. Proposed Criteria are pending and will be evaluated by a National Technical Committee. Criteria codes are discussed in Appendices II and III.

Species	Year	Season	Min	Max	Units	Proposed	Confirmed
Greater Sage-Grouse	2002	breeding	--	4,000	adults only	A1	NV1, NV3g
Gray Flycatcher	1999	breeding	1	4	pairs/km^{2*}		NV1
Loggerhead Shrike	1999	breeding	1	5	pairs/km^{2*}		NV1
Sage Thrasher	1999	breeding	5	43	pairs/km^{2*}		NV1
Vesper Sparrow	1999	breeding	5	43	pairs/km^{2*}		NV1
Sage Sparrow	1999	breeding	5	43	pairs/km^{2*}		NV1

*Density estimated in appropriate habitat and in the appropriate season.

Conservation Issues

Because of the remoteness of this area opportunities for anthropogenic disturbances are relatively limited. However, the area is a popular destination for ORV riders. As long as this use is well managed and users comply with regulations, the likelihood of resource damage is small. High Rock Canyon is closed from February 1 to April 15 to reduce disturbance to nesting raptors. The wilderness status of much of the area also reduces opportunities for disturbance, though many of the travel corridors are "cherry stemmed" in the wilderness and still open to travel. Again, as long as users stick to these designated travel routes and do not pioneer roads into wilderness, disturbance will be limited. As with other desert shrub communities in northern Nevada, the opportunity for landscape conversion to invasive annual grasses exists.

High Rock Canyon

Visiting the Site

The High Rock Resource Area IBA is remote and only those equipped for self-sufficient travel with a high clearance vehicle should journey into this area. The rewards for those willing to make the effort are spectacular. High Rock Canyon is accessible by vehicle (though closed seasonally January– mid-April) and is a great place to view raptors and a variety of sagebrush-steppe bird species. Other portions of the area require backcountry travel skills. If backpacking is your travel mode, an overnight trip in Little High Rock Canyon is also worth a trip.

Jarbidge Mountains

Area: 65,341 ha
UTM Easting: 634271
UTM Northing: 4630982

Description

Much of this IBA encompasses the 113,167 acre Jarbidge Wilderness Area, characterized by high mountains and deep glaciated canyons. It has 8 peaks over 10,000 feet, some of which drop to canyons 4,000 feet below. These mountains form a single crest and maintain elevations between 9,800 and 11,000 feet for about 7 miles. This area is unusually wet for Nevada, with seven to eight feet of snow falling annually, ideal for vegetation that varies from northern desert to alpine vegetation zones and includes mountain mahogany stands, conifer forests, aspen, riparian stringers along streams, wet meadows, montane shrubs, and grasslands. Many seeps, springs, creeks, and a few small lakes provide surface water for birds and other wildlife. There has been a history of sheep grazing in the Jarbidge Mountains and despite reductions in stocking levels the area is still over grazed by sheep and cattle, with associated trampling of riparian areas, soil erosion, and loss of grass cover (Wuerthner 1992).

The Jarbidge Mountains IBA is adjacent to the Mary's River IBA, whose headwaters form in the southern portion of the Jarbidge Mountains. Physiographically, the upper Mary's River is more closely allied with the Jarbidge Mountains than it is with the lower portion of the Mary's River. However, in considering IBA boundaries, functional systems, in this case united by a watershed, trumped the geographical alliance embraced by the Jarbidge Mountains. The decision was made to carve out a piece of the Jarbidge Mountains to be retained as the Mary's River IBA.

Land uses within the Jarbidge Mountains IBA include conservation, hunting and fishing, rangeland (livestock grazing), recreation and tourism, water supply, research, and wilderness.

Birds

The site supports a complete assemblage of high montane bird species, including Blue Grouse and Red Crossbill (two species poorly represented in other Nevada IBAs), Cassin's Finch, Hermit and Swainson's Thrushes, and Mountain Bluebird. Winter Wrens have also been documented singing in the Jarbidge Mountains during breeding season, though nests have not been found. Breeding outside of the Sierra Nevada remains to be confirmed. The riparian drainages found within the Jarbidge host significant numbers of songbirds. The higher elevation sagebrush tablelands host impressive numbers of Greater Sage-Grouse and are important brood rearing sites.

Species used to identify the Jarbidge Mountains IBA and the criteria met by the site. Density is derived from Breeding Bird Atlas surveys (GBBO 2002). Criteria codes are discussed in Appendix II.

Species	Year	Season	Density (pairs/km²)*		Units	Confirmed
			Min	Max		
MacGillivray's Warbler	2000	breeding	0	43	pairs	NV1
Sage Thrasher	1998	breeding	1	4	pairs	NV1
Vesper Sparrow	2000	breeding	1	43	pairs	NV1
Northern Goshawk	2000	breeding	0	1	pairs	NV1
Olive-sided Flycatcher	1998	breeding	0	1	pairs	NV1
Orange-crowned Warbler	1998	breeding	1	4	pairs	NV1
Red-naped Sapsucker	1999	breeding	1	4	pairs	NV1
Prairie Falcon	1997	breeding	0	1	pairs	NV1
Cooper's Hawk	1999	breeding	0	1	pairs	NV1
Black-throated Gray Warbler	1997	breeding	--	--	pairs	NV1

*Within suitable habitat for each species' life history needs.

Conservation Issues

Grazing management is a long-standing issue in this landscape. One consistent concern is that riparian corridors and aspen stands are disproportionately impacted by grazing when cattle congregate in these sensitive habitats.

Elk introductions have occurred in the Jarbidge Mountains and elk hunting is a popular activity in fall. From the standpoint of bird conservation the elk may not be an issue, but they certainly can become an issue if their numbers exceed the capacity of the range to support them. Elk have caused a disproportionately large impact on aspen elsewhere in their range, and in Nevada aspen is a critical and often degraded habitat type.

As with all Forest Service lands, ORV use poses a threat and will continue to do so until regulations for this user group are adopted and enforced. The site is relatively remote and therefore at the moment does not receive an excessive amount of attention from this user group. The fact that much of the area lies within designated wilderness also restricts this type of impact to the perimeter of the IBA.

Visiting the Site

There are many places in the Jarbidge IBA to enjoy birding, and the site accommodates the gamut of interests from those who prefer to bird from the car to anyone seeking to combine birding with a wilderness adventure. Bear Creek Summit, Jarbidge Canyon, and Biroth Ridge are all accessible by car. Biroth Ridge also has the option of a five-mile (potentially overnight) hike at the end of the road.

Aspen, conifers, and montane meadow in the Jarbidge Mountains IBA (© Bob Goodman)

Lahontan Valley Wetlands

Area: 174,172 ha
UTM Easting: 359357
UTM Northing: 4383843

Description

The Lahontan Valley Wetlands are a remnant of ancient Lake Lahontan, a Pleistocene lake that once covered 2,244,225 hectares (8,665 square miles) of western and northern Nevada. The lake reached its maximum extent about 14,000 years ago, then receded in stages as the climate in western North America entered an extended period of declining precipitation. The Lahontan Valley Wetlands began to emerge from the lake bed about 10,000 years ago (Chisholm and Neel 2002). Today, the wetlands form the most important waterfowl breeding and migratory site in Nevada and are critical to many species using the Pacific Flyway.

The wetlands of the valley experience varying levels of freshwater inputs and, coupled with evaporation, display varying concentrations of minerals. The result is remarkable diversity in the types of wetlands available to birds, from saline systems that support simple ecosystems similar to the Great Salt Lake, to freshwater marshes. To add to the variety, wetland depths can range from damp ephemeral playas to relatively deep marshes. Some of the more prominent features and critically important resources within the IBA include Stillwater NWR and Stillwater Wildlife Management Area, Carson Lake and Pasture, and Soda Lake. Depending on location within the Lahontan Valley Wetlands, the area serves as significant breeding habitat for many bird species (primarily waterbirds), critical stopover habitat for migrating birds, and wintering areas for waterfowl, raptors, and some passerines. The valley's climate is one of the warmest and driest in northern Nevada with an annual rainfall of only 5.32 inches. (Chipley et al. 2003)

Short-billed Dowitcher

The Lahontan Valley Wetlands were designated as a site in the Western Hemispheric Shorebird Reserve Network in 1988 (Manomet Center for Conservation Science 2004). The area has also been nominated to the Ramsar Delegation of Wetlands of Global Concern (Chisholm and Neel 2002).

In addition to wetlands, important habitat types in the Lahontan Valley IBA include low desert shrublands and agricultural fields (including irrigated crops and pastures and grasslands). Major land uses include agricultural production, hunting, military training (primarily aerial activity), nature conservation, wildlife research, tourism and recreation, and urban-suburban use and development.

Birds

Depending on water levels, the area is visited by up to 250,000 shorebirds, including Long-billed Dowitcher, Western and Least sandpipers, American Avocet, Wilson's Phalarope, and Long-billed Curlew (including about 60 breeding pairs), with peak numbers in the latter part of April, and again in the latter part of August.

Nearly a quarter of a million coots have been recorded in the fall. Migration also brings thousands of waterfowl, including Snow Goose and smaller numbers of Ross' and White-fronted geese, along with Gadwall, Northern Pintail, and Green-winged and Cinnamon Teal. The wetlands are particularly critical for Canvasback, with up to 28,000 recorded (more than half the Pacific Flyway population), and Redhead, with up to 29,000 recorded during migration. The area just upstream from the terminus of the Carson River acts as a migrant trap, particularly during the fall, and large numbers of raptors use the wetlands during the winter.

The wetlands are also important during the breeding season. As many as 10,000 White-faced Ibis forage in the Lahontan Valley. The 6,000 members of that population that reside on Stillwater NWR represent the world's largest colony. Up to 5,000 American Avocet remain to breed, as do close to 700 Snowy Plovers.

Species used to identify the Lahontan Valley Wetlands IBA and the criteria met by the site. Proposed Criteria are pending and will be evaluated by a National Technical Committee. Criteria codes are discussed in Appendices II and III.

Species	Year	Season	Min	Max	Units	Proposed	Confirmed
Eared Grebe	1987	migration	--	10,000	individuals		NV2, NV3a
White-faced Ibis	1987	breeding	--	10,000	adults only		NV1, NV2, NV3e
Canvasback	1982	migration	--	28,000	adults only		NV2, NV3g, NV3a
Redhead	1987	migration	--	25,000	individuals		NV2, NV3g, NV3a
Bald Eagle	1987	winter	--	70	individuals		NV1
Snowy Plover	1987	breeding	--	670	adults only	B1	NV1, NV2
Long-billed Dowitcher	1987	migration	--	100,000	adults only		NV2, NV3c
Black-necked Stilt	1987	migration	--	8,000	adults only		NV2, NV3c
American Avocet	1987	migration	--	60,000	adults only		NV1, NV2, NV3e
Wilson's Phalarope	1987	migration	--	10,000	adults only		NV2, NV3c

Conservation Issues

The Lahontan Valley wetlands have changed dramatically since the 1860s when the discovery of the Comstock Lode initiated mining activities, industrialization, and the development of ranches and concentrated settlements along the Carson River. The development of water diversions had mixed impacts on the wetlands. Water extracted from the Carson River starved the wetlands. Water diverted from the Truckee River for the Newlands Project in the early 1900s replenished some of what was taken from the Carson. The diversion also changed the timing of water delivery to the marshes. The timing does not necessarily correspond with the needs of breeding and migrating birds. The wetlands probably covered about 150,000 acres in the decade of 1850-1860, but today have shrunk to about 10,000 acres (Chisholm and Neel 2002). The condition of the Lahontan Valley Wetlands remains intimately linked with upstream activities on the Carson River and to some extent the Truckee River.

Water and the timing with which it is delivered to the marshes are critical issues. Nevada Public Law 101-618 includes a provision authorizing the restoration of a long-term average of 25,000 acres of wetlands through a water-rights acquisition program. The U.S. Fish and Wildlife Service, the State of Nevada, the Nevada Waterfowl Association, and The Nature Conservancy have all contributed to the purchase of water rights. The purchase of these water rights permits land managers to order water like any other water user, thus helping to moderate the peaks and troughs as well as the unpredictability of water availability. (Chisholm and Neel 2002)

Associated with water and perhaps linked in surprising ways is the delivery of contaminants into the system. Prior to the alteration of the hydrologic regime in the valley, poisonous heavy metals and alkaline salts concentrated in playa lakes as water evaporated in summer. Winds, of which Nevada has a surfeit, carried these contaminants away in clouds of aeolian dust. This natural cycle has been largely disrupted with the alteration of water flows. Inflow of agricultural contaminants from farm runoff and the influx of heavy metals (particularly mercury as a by-product from Comstock era mining) compound the problem. Currently, the only treatment for this situation relies on flushing of drain flows and sediments with high-quality water, coupled with the periodic draining and drying of water bodies (Chisholm and Neel 2002).

Soda Lake, a migration stopover site and potential breeding area for Snowy Plover, is under a patchwork of public and private ownership. This area has been under increasing residential development pressure, which could have negative impacts on the setting for birds. Unmanaged ORV use in the area may also be problematic and lead to habitat degradation and direct disturbance to nesting birds.

Visiting the Site

Some of the more popular bird watching destinations in the area have already been mentioned. Soda Lake is often worth a visit, particularly during spring and fall migration. The Diversion Dam near Ragtown is a popular spot for songbirds, dabbling ducks, and egrets and herons. Several areas for shorebirds are accessible by road, including Carson Lake and Pasture, and S-Line and Harmon reservoirs. Limited road access to Stillwater NWR lies at Stillwater Point. A project to install a boardwalk and blind is underway at Stillwater Point and will dramatically improve the visitor experience. Additional information and current conditions around the area can be obtained from the Stillwater NWR headquarters in Fallon.

Scouting for birds at Carson Lake and Pasture

Lake Mead

Area: 61786 ha
UTM Easting: 724567
UTM Northing: 3993258

Description

The Lake Mead IBA includes the lake portion of Lake Mead National Recreation Area, as defined by the mean pool elevation. The NRA actually extends well into adjacent uplands. The IBA encompasses over 142 miles of the former channel of the Colorado River and two artificial impoundments, Lake Mead and Lake Mojave. Adjacent uplands (not included in the IBA Boundary) include Mojave Desert vegetation types, with minor components of the Sonoran and Great Basin deserts present within the park. This landscape is primarily dominated by creosote and bursage. Cliffs abut many sections of the lake and provide critical nest sites for raptors.

American Avocet (© Richard S. Barrett)

As defined, the IBA is 100 percent open water. Land uses include tourism and recreation, water supply, wildlife conservation, fishing, and research.

Birds

This IBA was recognized principally for migration resting opportunities and wintering habitat for waterbirds. This type of use is often sporadic and birds can be highly dispersed, with such factors as food availability and prevailing winds determining which areas of the lakes will be utilized. The waters of the two lakes constitute the largest expanse of open water in the state and provide a critical resource for waterbirds.

The extent of this area poses a significant challenge to describing the avifaunal use of the site. A few accessible locations near population centers such as Las Vegas Bay and Overton Bay receive fairly frequent counts. The remainder of the lake receives little visitation from biologists or amateur birders. The National Park Service, which manages these sites, is attempting to fill this knowledge gap with more regular surveys of Lake Mead. Much of the data included in this description is derived from the first year of these survey efforts in 2004. The peak count in that effort came on April 7 and included 63 gulls and terns, 377 shorebirds and waders, and 2,210 waterfowl. Though this effort has already added tremendously to our understanding of how birds are using this landscape, the survey efforts do not cover the entire lake and therefore do not constitute a census of the area.

Species used to identify the Lake Mead IBA and the criteria met by the site. Proposed criteria await additional data prior to evaluation by the Nevada IBA TAC. Criteria codes are discussed in Appendix II.

Species	Year	Season	Min	Max	Units	Proposed	Confirmed
American White Pelican	2001	winter		450	individuals		NV1
American Avocet	2004	migration		591	individuals		NV1
Bald Eagle	2002	winter	--	79	individuals		NV1, NV3g
Peregrine Falcon	2002	breeding	9	11	pairs	NV3g	NV1
Southwest Willow Flycatcher	2002	breeding		15	pairs	NV3g	NV1
Western/Clark's Grebe	2002	migration, winter		587	individuals		NV1
Yellow-breasted Chat	2002	breeding					NV1
Lucy's Warbler	2002	breeding					NV1

Conservation Issues

Few conservation threats specific to migrating or wintering birds on the lakes have been identified. Recreational use of the lakes by motor boat or personal watercraft can be heavy, but peak use occurs during warm weather and not during migration or winter.

Water quantity and quality can be problematic. A recent drought cycle reduced water levels in the lake to the point of crisis for water users, but adequate water for wintering and migrating birds remained. Pollutants such as perchlorate that are entering the system are probably diluted to the point that they are not threatening bird populations, though cleanup is warranted for a variety of reasons and in the case of perchlorate, is ongoing. Lake Mead also receives treated effluent from the Las Vegas metropolitan area.

Conservation threats to adjacent land areas are more pressing and include invasive plant species, ORV use, and feral burros. These threats are being addressed by the National Park Service.

American White Pelican (© Richard S. Barrett)

Visiting the Site

Depending on time and a visitor's level of commitment, several options exist for bird watching around the Lake Mead IBA. Las Vegas Bay is probably the most accessible point and can be reached by automobile. The bay is the outflow point for Las Vegas Wash, and it often has a good diversity of waterbirds resting in the sheltered waters. Overton Beach, at the end of the Valley of Fire Road, is also another readily accessible area. The more intrepid may choose to join a commercial raft trip through Black Canyon (good area for raptors) or launch their own boat and explore the numerous inlets and bays around Lake Mead or Lake Mohave.

Mary's River

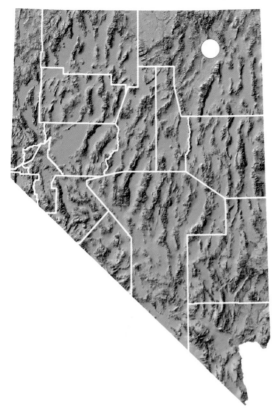

Area: 26,113 ha
UTM Easting: 642696
UTM Northing: 4588596

Description

The Mary's River is the primary tributary to the Humboldt River that drains the southern end of the Jarbidge Mountain Range in Elko County. It is located southeast of the town of Jarbidge and west of Wells. Its confluence with the Humboldt River is approximately 33 miles east of Elko. Ownership is primarily BLM, USFS, and private. The Mary's River watershed is a valuable area for river riparian and upland habitats. In 1991, most of this 57,980 hectare (220 square mile) area was protected from growing season livestock grazing and is responding vigorously to this protection. The area provides habitat for over 100 breeding bird species and several migratory and wintering bird species as well. The river is passable by canoe in the spring of the year and has reasonable road or trail access. The river's headwaters lie in designated USFS wilderness and much of the river is currently being considered as a candidate for Wild and Scenic River status. Two MAPS (banding) stations and one Watchable Wildlife site are found on the river.

Land uses within the Mary's River IBA include conservation, agriculture (seasonal grazing, native hay meadow cultivation), tourism and recreation, and water supply.

Birds

At various times of the year the river corridor sustains significant densities of White-faced Ibis, Cooper's Hawk, Northern Goshawk, Swainson's Hawk, Prairie Falcon, Greater Sandhill Crane, Long-billed Curlew, Short-eared Owl, Calliope Hummingbird, Lewis's Woodpecker, Red-naped Sapsucker, Willow Flycatcher (*E. t. brewsteri, E. t. adastus*), Loggerhead Shrike, Sage Thrasher, Orange-crowned Warbler, Virginia's Warbler, Black-throated Gray Warbler,

MacGillivray's Warbler, Wilson's Warbler, Yellow-breasted Chat, Vesper Sparrow, Sage Sparrow, Bobolink, and Greater Sage-Grouse.

In particular, the cottonwood-alder gallery is a rare and threatened habitat type in the state. Here, it is rebounding. Bird species such as Lewis' Woodpecker, Red-naped Sapsucker, Bullock's Oriole, Warbling Vireo, Yellow Warbler, and House Wren are responding positively.

A second key habitat that is an exceptional representative of the natural Humboldt System is the native wetland meadows. These provide significant nesting habitat for Bobolinks, Greater Sandhill Cranes, and Short-eared Owls. As emergent vegetation types (rushes and cattails) continue to respond to rest in the oxbow sloughs associated with the native meadows, Black Tern, Common Yellowthroat, Marsh Wren, and White-faced Ibis nesting numbers will respond in turn.

The Mary's River watershed is, to a great extent, the last functioning, natural relict representing what the entire Humboldt River system used to be. It is for that reason an exceptional site to provide for the continued existence of northern Nevada's native bird fauna and as a native plant stock source for additional avian recovery sites downstream on the main stem of the Humboldt. The Mary's River also constitutes an unbroken, 50-mile long willow-lined bird migration corridor.

Other key species at this site include Gadwall, Mallard, and Common Merganser, all of which breed here in remarkable numbers.

Species used to identify the Mary's River IBA and the criteria met by the site. Proposed criteria await evaluation by the National Technical Committee (A1) or the Nevada IBA TAC pending the availability of additional data. Criteria codes are discussed in Appendices II and III.

Species	Year	Season	Min	Max	Units	Proposed	Confirmed
Snowy Egret	2003	non-br	0	400	individuals	NV2, NV3g	NV3e
Greater Sage-Grouse	2003	resident	1,000	1,500	individuals	A1	NV1, NV3g
Sandhill Crane	2003	breeding	100	150	individuals		NV1, NV3g
Wilson's Phalarope	2003	breeding	0	20,000	individuals		NV3g, NV3c
Forster's Tern	2003	breeding	0	200	individuals		NV3gv
Lewis's Woodpecker	2003	breeding	200	250	individuals	NV2, NV3g	NV1
Sage Thrasher	2003	breeding	4,000	5,000	individuals		NV1
Yellow-breasted Chat	2003	breeding	3,000	4,000	individuals	NV3g	NV1, NV2
Bobolink	2003	breeding	2,000	3,000	individuals		NV1, NV2, NV3g

Conservation Issues

Invasive plant species include exotic thistle, tall whitetop, bur buttercup, and cheatgrass. The problem plants are being treated with chemicals.

Livestock numbers have been well managed on the private property portion of the IBA. Threats to habitat from poorly managed livestock grazing, gravel mining, or stream channelization are well regulated. Disturbance to bird populations remains low, with the possible exception of the convergence of haying dates and Bobolink, crane, phalarope, harrier and Short-eared Owl incubation dates. Off-road vehicle use increases every year. As rates of use

Beaver ponds and willows on the upper Mary's River

increase, so too do rates of abuse. This use will need to be examined in the near future and monitored for long-term impacts.

Landscapes in northeastern Nevada seem particularly vulnerable to conversion by fire. The pattern is an active summer fire season, typically spawned by dry lightening storms. Because much of the area is remote and water is scarce, fire control is difficult. Invasive species, particularly cheatgrass, become established in the wake of the fires and change the fire cycles in favor of annual grasses. Fire in the Mary's River watershed should be actively controlled and reseeding of burned areas with native seed a high agency priority.

Visiting the Site

The most accessible portion of this IBA is Cabin Field, a Watchable Wildlife site just north of I-80 and east of Elko. The IBA and river above this point is private land and not open to the public. To reach the upper river, which is again public lands, start at Deeth (Exit 333 from I-80) and take the Oneil Deeth Co Road north. In the vicinity of Current Creek, cross the Mary's River and make your way up towards the headwaters. The scenery is extraordinary in this area, the river is gorgeous, and the wildlife viewing is outstanding. It is also easy to get lost, and this area should only be explored with a high clearance vehicle and good BLM or USGS topographic maps. Another excellent option is departing from this area and backpacking up the Mary's River and into the Jarbidge Wilderness Area.

Meadow Valley Wash

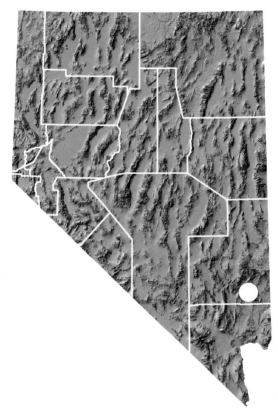

Area: 6,085 ha
UTM Easting: 717093
UTM Northing: 4120004

Description

Meadow Valley Wash drains a significant part of eastern Nevada, ultimately flowing into the Muddy River and Lake Mead. "Drain" and "flow" may be misleading terms in this desert setting, as surface water is rarely continuous through this drainage. The terms may be more appropriate in describing the movement of birds, particularly during migration, along this narrow, north-south riparian corridor. Meadow Valley Wash is 110 miles long, rising in the mountainous region of eastern Lincoln County, flowing south through Panaca and Caliente, into the Muddy River between Moapa and Glendale. The IBA has been identified as that portion of Meadow Valley Wash from approximately the Lincoln - Clark County line to just below Caliente to the north.

Land ownership is primarily federal (BLM), though there are some scattered private parcels in the wash. A Union Pacific Railroad right-of-way and rail line runs along the wash.

Wetlands and seeps ranging from tens to hundreds of acres are intermittent with the wash. This combination of large area, north-south alignment, and wetland sites make the wash a significant wildlife habitat and migration corridor for riparian and desert species. The wash provides bird habitat for year-round residents, seasonal breeding birds, and migrants.

The long, narrow shape of this IBA makes calculating the distribution of cover types difficult. Habitat can be described broadly as a complex mix of Mojave and Great Basin desert shrubs and shrub-steppe, with some limited woodlands and riparian habitats. A small percentage of the area has been converted to agricultural uses.

Birds

Meadow Valley Wash is one of a few desert riparian sites in southern Nevada. Although altered from its native condition, the site still provides breeding and stopover habitat for landbirds. Much interest from USFWS, BLM, Nevada Department of Wildlife, and TNC has been focused on the wash with an eye towards controlling invasive plants and enhancing habitat values for Neotropical migrants and other desert wildlife. The orientation of the site as a long, narrow corridor intuitively offers critical support for migrating birds, though this has yet to be documented other than anecdotally. Meadow Valley Wash actually drains a much larger region of eastern Nevada and probably funnels migrants to and from an extensive area; the current boundaries include the highest quality habitat in the wash.

Species used to identify the Meadow Valley Wash IBA and the criteria met by the site. Proposed Criteria are pending and will be evaluated by a Nevada IBA TAC when more data become available. Criteria codes are discussed in Appendix II.

Species	Year	Season	Min	Max	Units	Proposed	Confirmed
Willow Flycatcher	1999	breeding	0	4	individuals	NV1, NV3g	
Ash-throated Flycatcher	2002	migration	0	24	individuals	NV2, NV3f	NV1
Phainopepla	2001	resident	0	60	individuals	NV2, NV3f	NV1
Western Bluebird	2000	resident	0	30	individuals		NV1
Blue Grosbeak	2002	breeding	0	37	individuals	NV2	NV1
Yellow-breasted Chat	2002	resident	0	36	individuals	NV2, NV3f	NV1

Conservation Issues

As with every riparian system in the state, invasive plants are a concern. In the Meadow Valley Wash system invasive species include tamarisk, Russian olive, and annual grasses. Some disturbance to birds, particularly nesting species, is possible from human activities along the wash. However, the current risk from this source is believed to be low. The BLM has secured a grant from the Southern Nevada Public Land Management Act to apply towards a riparian habitat conservation management plan for this site.

Groundwater pumping is an ever-growing concern for all of the counties surrounding Las Vegas. The ever-thirsty megalopolis is looking to satisfy water needs by mining groundwater from several basins and significant aquifers in southern Nevada. The consequences of this pumping are poorly understood but could include loss of all surface waters due to draw-down and alteration of hydrological regimes. This is believed to be an extreme threat to this IBA.

Visiting the Site

NV 317, south of Caliente, follows Meadow Valley Wash for many miles, though this road was recently flood damaged, and whether and when it will be repaired is uncertain.

Moapa Valley

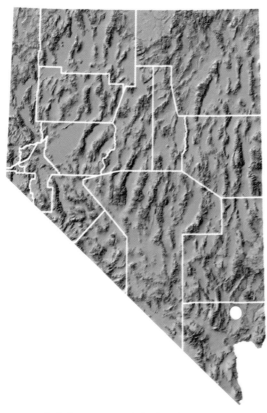

Area: 970 ha
UTM Easting: 705088
UTM Northing: 4065404

Description

This IBA encompasses the Moapa Valley and the upper reaches of the Muddy River. The area is striking in its setting in a vast expanse of sparse, mesic, Mojave Desert vegetation. Upon descending into the valley, the visitor is immediately struck by the lushness of the area, as the original Mormon settlers surely were. With a tall grove of *Washingtonia* palms surrounding the site of the now-defunct Warm Springs Resort, this corner of the valley could almost pass for a classic desert oasis from the reels of Lawrence of Arabia.

Extensive research in the area has revealed that most of the bird activity is concentrated on the Warm Springs Ranch. The Muddy River flows through this ranch and supports a narrow, lush band of riparian vegetation. Irrigation canals for the ranch transport water around the valley floor and support stringers of cottonwoods, willows, and tamarisk. Interspersed among the trees are fallowing pastures (the area is no longer grazed) and stands of screwbean mesquite. Land uses within the Moapa Valley IBA include agricultural uses, water management, and urban-suburban development.

Birds

Moapa Valley supports a breeding population of the Southwestern Willow Flycatcher. Other significant breeding birds include Western Yellow-billed Cuckoo and Phainopepla. The site has been documented as a migration stopover for passerines, and numerous raptor species winter in the valley. No single species appears on the site in large numbers, though some priority conservation species like the Southwestern Willow Flycatcher occur in such low numbers in the state that a concentration of a few birds quickly becomes significant. Overall, it is the assemblage of species here that is remarkable, an assemblage that is characteristic of a rare habitat type in Nevada. It is primarily this latter feature which distinguished the site and warranted its recognition as an IBA.

Additional bird species of interest include Sandhill Crane, Blue Grosbeak, Yellow-breasted Chat, and Lucy's Warbler. Some interesting rarities have shown up in Moapa Valley including Red-shouldered Hawk, Common Black-Hawk, and Mississippi Kite.

Species used to identify the Moapa Valley IBA and the criteria met by the site. Proposed criteria await additional data prior to evaluation by the Nevada IBA TAC. Criteria codes are discussed in Appendix II.

Species	Year	Season	Min	Max	Units	Proposed	Confirmed
Southwestern Willow Flycatcher	2005	breeding	2	--	pairs		NV1
Yellow-billed Cuckoo	2001	breeding	--	22	adults only		NV1, NV2, NV3g
Phainopepla	2001	breeding	--	158	adults only	NV3g	NV1, NV2

Conservation Issues

Significant parcels of land critical to the long-term stewardship of this IBA are not secure. In fact, at this writing, a private owner of a large critical parcel is looking for a developer to purchase the land. If this parcel were to be converted to houses, the quality of habitat could be compromised to the point that the site would no longer warrant IBA status. Agencies and nonprofit organizations have been attempting for years to find conservation buyers or to purchase properties under various land acquisition programs in order to assure long-term stewardship of this valley.

Groundwater pumping may be the second greatest threat facing this landscape. As with other sites in proximity to Las Vegas, this area could fall victim to pumping to supply the needs of the thirsty city. Proposals currently on the table could lead to large-scale groundwater pumping in numerous southern Nevada basins, with unknown consequences for existing surface waters.

Wherever water occurs in Nevada you can be sure that invasive plants are also a concern. Here tamarisk and Russian olive are problematic and have the potential to impact water availability. At some point in the history of this valley *Washingtonia* palms were imported and planted. These are most prominently visible at the tiny Moapa Valley NWR, formerly the Warm Springs Resort. Because these trees are impacting the habitat for the Moapa Dace, the endangered fish for which the refuge was established, it is likely that the trees will be removed, a change that will have little impact on native birds.

Visiting the Site

The most bird-rich portions of Moapa Valley IBA are privately owned lands that are not open to public visitation.

Monitor Valley

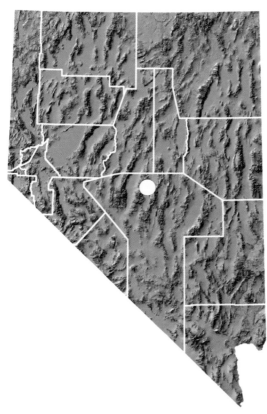

Area: 235,092 ha
UTM Easting: 525797
UTM Northing: 4305745

Description

Monitor Valley is located in central Nevada, southeast of Austin and northeast of Tonopah. The valley sits between the Toquima Range to the west and the Monitor Range to the east. The IBA includes Monitor Valley, the adjacent east slope of the Toquimas, and the adjacent west slope of the Monitors. The southern boundary of the IBA is located near the historic town of Belmont, the northern boundary is located in the valley at Potts Well, between Bald Mountain to the east and Pete's Summit to the west.

Monitor Valley is comprised primarily of federal land. The Toquima and Monitor ranges are Forest Service lands and are administered by the Humboldt-Toiyabe National Forest, Tonopah Ranger District. Monitor Valley is BLM land administered by the Tonopah Resource Area. Both the Forest Service and BLM lands contain private inholdings that collectively total approximately 2,590 ha (6,400 acres).

Lower elevations within the Monitor Valley IBA are covered by sagebrush-dominated shrublands and include areas of sagebrush-steppe. At slightly higher elevations and reaching to mid-mountain are piñon-juniper forests. Perennial streams enter both sides of the valley from the Monitor and Toquima ranges and support narrow montane riparian corridors. Aspen stands also add to the diversity of this landscape. Land uses here include rangeland, hunting and fishing, conservation, tourism and recreation, and wilderness.

Birds

Monitor Valley and the adjacent mountain ranges support over a dozen Nevada Partners in Flight priority species, including one of Nevada's most significant Greater Sage-Grouse populations. Other key species include MacGillivray's and Black-throated Gray warblers, Sage Sparrow, Sage Thrasher, Pinyon Jay, Gray Flycatcher, Red-naped Sapsucker, Loggerhead Shrike, and Western Bluebird.

The Monitor Valley is a long way from Nevada's major population centers. This relative isolation provides added protection for the habitat types and associated plant and animal species present at this IBA.

Species used to identify the Monitor Valley IBA and the criteria met by the site. Proposed criteria await evaluation by the National Technical Committee. Codes for criteria are discussed beginning on page 5 and in Appendix III.

Species	Year	Season	Min	Max	Units	Proposed	Confirmed
Greater Sage-Grouse	2002	breeding	--	2,000	breeding pairs	A1	NV1,NV3g

Conservation Issues

Cheatgrass and other non-native plant species associated with disturbance, specifically fire and grazing, have taken hold in this landscape. The interaction between fire and grazing is a mechanism for habitat conversion in the Great Basin, transitioning landscapes from shrublands to monocultures dominated by annual grass.

There is potential for disturbance to birds or their habitat as recreational use of Monitor Valley and the adjoining mountain ranges increases. This disturbance is primarily manifested through unregulated ORV use that both destroys and fragments habitat.

Visiting the Site

Though remoteness precludes a spontaneous visit, the abundance of public land in the Monitor Valley IBA welcomes visitation. Several perennial streams drain towards the valley and several of these waterways have trails that invite exploration, either as a day trip or overnight hike. These include Pine, Barley, and Mosquito Creeks. Hiking into the Table Mountain or the Alta Toquima wildernesses will provide access to species characteristic of higher elevation habitats.

Rain returns to Monitor Valley after a long dry summer

Mount Grant

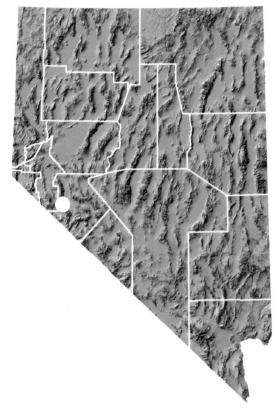

Area: 37,625 ha
UTM Easting: 341673
UTM Northing: 4268198

Description

Mount Grant looms
dramatically above the
western shoreline of Walker
Lake. The majority of the site
is managed by the
Hawthorne Army Depot, the
western portion by the BLM,
with some private lands
(primarily patented mining
claims) on the southern end.
Most of the recognized IBA
has not been grazed in over
70 years. The area is
topographically diverse and
geologically complex. The
Nature Conservancy
identified four riparian and
nine upland plant
communities on Mount
Grant, including mixed shrub
scrub, great basin sagebrush
scrub, cottonwood riparian forest, aspen forest, piñon woodland, juniper
woodland, mountain mahogany woodland, willow riparian scrub, montane
meadow, mountain sagebrush scrub, low sagebrush scrub, subalpine pine forest,
and alpine scrub. Perennial streams include Cottonwood, Dutch, Squaw, Rose,
House, Cat, and Lapon creeks. The plant communities are in good-to-excellent
condition, serving as ecological baselines for similar habitats elsewhere in the
Great Basin.

Land use within the Mount Grant IBA is primarily dedicated to military needs.
Following the terrorist attacks of September 2001 on New York, security was
tightened at this and other military installations. Access to Mount Grant is now
tightly controlled. As such, the landscape is little visited and access is granted
only to the occasional organized field trip. Looking both at the closed military
area and surrounding lands, land use includes conservation, research, hunting,
military uses, rangelands, and water management.

Birds

The importance of the site for Nevada birds lies in the exemplary condition of
the habitat, which supports a high diversity of upland bird species as well as
riparian species. Because the military portion has not been grazed in over 70

years (possibly unique in Nevada), the habitat is in such good condition that it serves as a standard for comparison for these Great Basin plant and associated bird communities. There is potential for research on these ecosystems that can be of high value in conservation of Great Basin bird communities. Other key species at Mount Grant include Sage Thrasher, Sage Sparrow, and Pinyon Jay.

Species used to identify the Mount Grant IBA and the criteria met by the site. Proposed criteria await evaluation by the National Technical Committee (A1), or availability of additional data for the Nevada IBA TAC. Criteria codes are discussed starting on page 5 and in Appendix III.

Species	Year	Season	Min	Max	Units	Proposed	Confirmed
Greater Sage-Grouse	2002	breeding	300	500	individuals	A1, NV2, NV3g	NV1
Sage Sparrow	1999	breeding	0	274	individuals	NV2	NV1

Conservation Issues

Because of the Department of Defense (DoD) management of most of this landscape, current threats to the integrity of the habitat are believed to be low. As with most landscapes in Nevada, the potential for invasive plant species, in this case particularly cheatgrass, to become established and change vegetative communities is ever a possibility. However, the absence of livestock grazing is one element of the invasion cycle has been removed from the picture. Hawthorne Army Depot manages most of this site to protect watershed values. While this is largely consistent with protecting habitat quality and wildlife values, the current management strategy is not guaranteed in perpetuity.

Visiting the Site

Following the attacks of September 11, 2001, much of the Mount Grant area was closed to public access. Unless this policy changes, visiting the bird-rich portions of the site is not possible.

North Ruby Valley

Area: 20,328 ha
UTM Easting: 646602
UTM Northing: 4498429

Description

The North Ruby Valley is one of four remarkable landscapes identified as IBAs in close proximity in central and southern Elko County. To the south lie Franklin Lake and Ruby Lake NWR IBAs, and to the west, Ruby Mountains IBA. North Ruby Valley is a relatively flat, high desert valley nestled between the Ruby Mountains and the East Humboldt Range. The site is a mixture of wetlands, including willow and cottonwood stringers, and adjacent upland desert shrub habitats.

Most of the birds characterizing this site are attracted to a series of native grass and hay meadows along the east toe of the Ruby Mountains and the western toe of the East Humboldt Range. The sites are well watered in most years by snow melt from these adjacent ranges. Active management for more than a century by several private ranches has likely increased the extent of this habitat type at the site and fostered the remarkable bird community. Because of the nature of the runoff, timing of green-up, delayed haying, and the practice of moving stock out of the pastures at a time that corresponds to bird breeding season, grassland birds here pull off broods largely undisturbed. Land ownership at this site is about 85 percent private, with the remaining lands along the east and west boundaries managed by the BLM and the US Forest Service. Land use in the North Ruby Valley IBA is agricultural and includes grazing and hay production.

Birds

This site supports the highest density of breeding Long-billed Curlews yet recorded in North America (L. Oring, University of Nevada, Reno, pers. comm.). The research that Dr. Oring and his doctoral student Alex Hartman are conducting here is revealing many remarkable traits about this species. What makes this site unique and so well suited for the curlews is the way in which the ranches are managed. The extent of native hay meadows has likely increased due to the manipulation of water across the sites. Further, cattle graze these pastures in late fall and winter and are moved off during (bird) breeding season. The fields are wet enough during this time period that people rarely venture into them, thus leaving the birds largely undisturbed.

Species used to identify the North Ruby Valley IBA and the criteria met by the site. Proposed criteria await review by the National Technical Committee. Codes for criteria are discussed starting on page 5 and in Appendices II and III.

Species	Year	Season	Min	Max	Proposed	Confirmed
Greater Sage-Grouse	2003	breeding	1,946	2,335	A1	NV1, NV3g
Long-billed Curlew	2005	breeding	--	500	A1	NV1, NV3g
Bald Eagle	2005	breeding	--	2		NV1

Greater Sage-Grouse are also an important component of this site. The Ruby Valley population of sage grouse is estimated to number between 1,946 and 2,335 birds using about 45 leks (Nevada Department of Wildlife 2004). This represents about three percent of the state's sage grouse population. Most (ca. 90 percent) of these leks lie within the boundary of this IBA.

Numerous Nevada Partners in Flight priority species breed in this landscape and contribute to its value as an IBA. Although the occurrence of these species is documented, their absolute numbers are not, and more field work needs to be done to assess population densities. Key species include Short-eared Owl, Sandhill Crane, Wilson's Phalarope, Cooper's Hawk, Swainson's Hawk, White-faced Ibis, Olive-sided Flycatcher, Willow Flycatcher, Gray Flycatcher, Ash-throated Flycatcher, Loggerhead Shrike, Western Bluebird, Sage Thrasher, Vesper Sparrow, Sage Sparrow, Orange-crowned Warbler, Wilson's Warbler, and Bobolink.

North Ruby Valley IBA (© Bob Goodman)

Conservation Issues

Invasive species, specifically non-native plants, pose a threat to this site. Most of the wet meadow habitat is too wet for cheatgrass, but this species is well established on drier upland sites where it has already interacted with fire cycles to begin forming a monoculture. In drier years less vegetative cover for breeding birds means a higher rate of predation, particularly on nests and pre-fledging birds. Strong evidence suggests that the local coyote population has effectively focused on Sandhill Cranes as prey, and this behavior appears to be transmitted to successive generations (J. Mackay, Ruby Lake NWR, pers. comm.). Finally, there is concern that water rights could be sold or otherwise acquired and water moved out of the valley, where current water uses are highly beneficial to wildlife.

Visiting the Site

Because this IBA is almost entirely in private property, viewing opportunities are limited to roadside observation along NV 229. The same suite of species at North Ruby Valley IBA are also present at Franklin Lake and Ruby Lake NWR IBAs immediately to the south, so visitors may wish to focus their efforts at the latter locations.

Western Bluebirds (© Bob Goodman)

Northern Snake Range

Area: 20,531 ha
UTM Easting: 742059
UTM Northing: 4349668

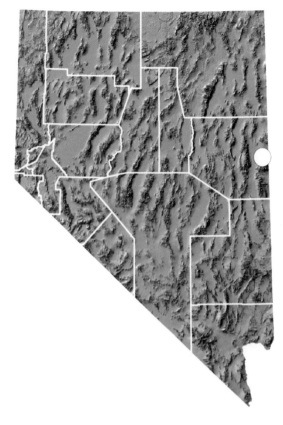

Description

The Snake Range is divided into a northern and southern region by US 6/50. The core of the southern Snake Range comprises the Great Basin National Park IBA and, in addition to being managed by different entities, the two areas present subtle differences. The Great Basin National Park IBA has higher elevations and consistently supports a suite of birds typically associated with subalpine and alpine habitats. While many of these same habitats exist around Mount Moriah in the northern Snake Range, to date the associated bird species have not been found. One hypothesis to explain this absence, particularly given the close proximity of the region to the Great Basin National Park IBA, is that the extent of the subalpine and alpine habitat is too small to sustain populations of the key bird species. The Northern Snake Range IBA is exemplary for other reasons.

The Northern Snake Range IBA is characterized by a high plateau bounded by rugged cliffs and steep canyons. The plateau region supports montane meadow, mountain mahogany-fir-pine forests, montane shrub, and aspen stands. Springs and seeps scattered across the plateau contribute to habitat heterogeneity. The aspens and mountain meadows may be particularly noteworthy, given the health of these systems. The meadows sustain a mix of grasses, forbes, and shrubs (mostly sagebrush), and the aspen stands are multi-aged with numerous cavities. Mount Moriah dominates the skyline with its 12,067 foot summit and its shoulders cloaked in alpine vegetation. The noteworthy birds are those associated with the slightly lower and aforementioned habitat types.

The 82,000 acre Mount Moriah Wilderness Area covers much of the IBA. This wilderness has unique qualities and several special attractions. The rugged terrain and lack of access provide many opportunities for solitude and wilderness experiences. Mount Moriah, at an elevation of 12,050 feet and adjacent 1,000-acre plateau known as The Table are the center of the wilderness attractions. The Table is a unique high-elevation plateau covered with subalpine vegetation, and ancient bristlecone and limber pine stands occur along its edge. All recreation use occurs as dispersed activities. Hunting is the major activity, followed by hiking, fishing, photography, camping, sightseeing, and wildlife viewing. There are no developed sites in the area.

Mount Moriah Wilderness is the home of one known sensitive plant species (*Eriogeron cavernensis*), and is suspected of having other Threatened, Endangered, rare, or sensitive plant species. Bonneville cutthroat trout survive in perennial streams and Rocky Mountain bighorn sheep bands roam the rocky shoulders of Mount Moriah. Blue Grouse and Greater Sage-Grouse are also found in the area. Land uses in the Northern Snake Range IBA include rangeland (grazing allotments), nature and wildlife conservation, hunting and fishing, designated wilderness, and other forms of recreation and tourism.

Birds

The Northern Snake Range receives relatively little visitation and, as such bird-related data are scarce. Readily apparent to any visitor, however, is the quality of the habitat the site offers. Little impacted by the suite of ills plaguing public lands, most areas remain accessible only by foot or horseback. This is a typical sky island, surrounded by expanses of desert to the east and west. Aspen stands are multi-aged, show active regeneration and support primary and secondary cavity nesters. Conifer forests are highly diverse with complex structure (under-, mid-, overstory). The montane parkland has excellent grass and forb components with varying densities of shrubs. Available data indicate that the suite of bird species one would expect to encounter in these habitat types are well represented.

Species used to identify the Northern Snake Range IBA and the criteria met by the site. Criteria codes are discussed in Appendix II.

Species	Year	Season	Density (pairs/km²)*		Units	Confirmed
			Min	Max		
Cooper's Hawk	2000	breeding	0	4	pairs	NV1
Northern Goshawk	1998	breeding	0	1	pairs	NV1
Three-toed Woodpecker	1999	breeding	0	4	pairs	NV1
Pinyon Jay	1998	breeding	5	43	pairs	NV1
Juniper Titmouse	2000	breeding	1	43	pairs	NV1
Black-throated Gray Warbler	2000	breeding	0	43	pairs	NV1
MacGillivray's Warbler	1998	breeding	1	4	pairs	NV1
Vesper Sparrow	2000	breeding	5	43	pairs	NV1
Sage Sparrow	2000	breeding	1	4	pairs	NV1

*Within suitable habitat for each species' life history needs.

Conservation Issues

Until the Humboldt-Toiyabe National Forest establishes ORV regulations, ORVs will be a threat to public lands. However, in the areas visited by the nominator, travel has been well confined to designated travel corridors, though some incursions into the designated wilderness area have occurred. Grazing activity should continue to be monitored and regulated to maintain the high value of these habitats. A visit during a particularly dry fall (2001) found many areas severely grazed and suggested that cattle probably should have been removed earlier in the season. However, in subsequent years the most heavily impacted areas observed that year seemed to have rebounded reasonably well. Careful oversight by the Forest Service and the cooperating leasee is warranted due to the importance of this site.

Elk have been introduced to this area. The herd does not seem to be exerting undue pressure on the aspen stands. However, it is well known that unregulated elk herds can significantly alter aspen and willow habitats (e.g., Able 2003). Aspen stands should be closely monitored and harvest regulations modified accordingly to maintain the balance between herd numbers and health and the condition of the aspen stands.

Visiting the Site

Because this site sits on the top of a high plateau, options for reaching the area are few. Hikers and horseback riders access the area from Hendry's Creek on the southeast side of the range. Another option for a traveler with a high clearance vehicle is to drive up to the plateau from Six Mile Canyon on the east side of the range.

Mountain meadow and aspens below Mount Moriah

Oasis Valley

Area: 7,347 ha
UTM Easting: 523940
UTM Northing: 4089830

Description

For birds, Oasis Valley could not be more aptly named. Birds migrating between the Mojave Desert and the Great Basin rely on Oasis Valley as one of the rare routes that guarantees water. The Amargosa River (a misnomer, except during flash floods every decade or so) winds through Oasis Valley and is classified as ephemeral; however, there are short stretches of permanent water. Elsewhere in the valley, numerous springs, wetlands and farm ponds support an important flyway and a riparian corridor with the town of Beatty at its center. The riparian corridor is surrounded by upland transitional vegetation of the Mojave Desert and Great Basin scrub ecotones. Most of the valley floor is privately owned (including two Nature Conservancy acquisitions) and the Beatty Habitat Committee is working on restoration of the riparian and spring systems within the valley. The BLM manages lands adjacent to the valley floor, including the Bullfrog Hills to the west and the Bare Mountains to the southeast.

Land uses within the Oasis Valley IBA include agriculture, conservation and research, urban-suburban development, and light commercial development.

Birds

A successful migration by landbirds moving through the area is likely to include passage through either Oasis Valley or Pahranagat Valley to the east. Although there are some areas of tamarisk, the riparian areas throughout the valley are to a large extent one of the healthiest examples throughout southern Nevada. With the Town of Beatty working hard to protect these areas, this site offers birds a reliable safe-haven to rest and refuel before continuing their migratory journey.

Bird banding efforts in the valley revealed that the site is particularly remarkable for the numbers of four species of migrating warblers.

Species used to identify the Oasis Valley IBA and the criteria met by the site. Proposed criteria await the availability of additional data before further review by the Nevada IBA TAC. Criteria codes are discussed in Appendix II.

Species	Year	Season	Min	Max	Units	Proposed	Confirmed
Yellow-billed cuckoo	2002	breeding	0	2	breeding pairs	NV3g	NV1, NV2
Willow Flycatcher	2001	breeding	1	--	adults		NV1, NV2
Yellow Warbler	2001	migration	--	5,000	adults		NV3g, NV3f
MacGillivray's Warbler	2001	migration	--	5,000	adults		NV1, NV3g, NV3f
Common Yellowthroat	2001	migration	--	5,000	adults		NV3g, NV3f
Wilson's Warbler	2001	migration	--	10,000	adults		NV1, NV3g, NV3f

Conservation Issues

Oasis Valley is in something of a state of flux. A number of large, privately owned parcels have come on the market in recent years. For at least some of these parcels, TNC has been interested in seeing them conserved but has been constrained by pricing issues, and by an unwillingness to acquire too much private property in the valley. Of greater preference would be matching a conservation buyer with a willing seller.

Most of the private land holdings north of Beatty are or have been associated with livestock ranching operations. Intensification or expansion of these operations could lead to increased impacts on habitat quality. Given the extended drought in the region, an increase in stocking rates is unlikely.

Wilson's Warbler (© Bob Goodman)

However, the valley holds some of the only available water and forage for miles around, so operators moving their stock into the valley because of poor range conditions elsewhere could have a disproportionate impact on the local area.

Invasive plants and animals are a significant problem in Oasis Valley. Tamarisk is well established, but eradication efforts have increased significantly in recent years and are meeting with initial success.

As with other areas within an alarmingly-wide radius of Las Vegas, water developers have had their eye on aquifers beneath Nye County. Extensive studies need to be conducted prior

Tour group visits the Amargosa River

to concluding that groundwater pumping would have no impact on above-ground flows. Oasis Valley relies on many seeps and springs, and a high water table that sustains cottonwoods, willows, and the few velvet ash trees remaining in the valley. Also noteworthy is the fact that Ash Meadows NWR IBA lies just "downstream" from Oasis Valley. Groundwater pumping in the Amargosa aquifer could severely damage both locations.

With careful planning and implementation, the Beatty Habitat Committee's plans to increase destination tourism can be compatible with maintaining and improving bird and wildlife habitat.

Visiting the Site

US 95 goes through the middle of the Oasis Valley IBA and there are several opportunities to explore the area. The Torrance Ranch, a Nature Conservancy property, lies on the east side of the highway and is open to the public. South of Beatty lies an area known as The Narrows, where the Amargosa River supports a string of cottonwoods. This is also a good area to explore, including both the riparian area and the adjacent uplands. As part of their effort to promote ecotourism, the Beatty Habitat Committee has developed a brochure that provides suggestions for birding opportunities and an area checklist. As the Beatty Habitat Committee's plans are implemented, more opportunities for hiking and exploring the area will become available.

Pahranagat Valley Complex

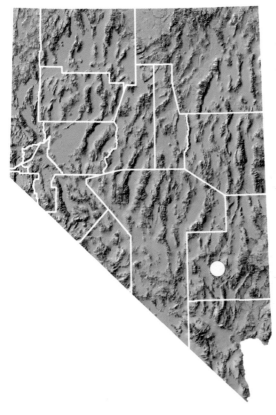

Area: 3,474 ha
UTM Easting: 661837
UTM Northing: 4139908

Description

The Pahranagat Valley Complex encompasses two important features in Pahranagat Valley, the Pahranagat Valley NWR on the south end of the complex and the Key Pittman Wildlife Management Area (WMA) at the north. These two publicly owned land parcels are separated by several private ranches. Private lands contribute to the integrity of the site and landowner cooperation and bird-friendly management practices on these parcels are long-term goals of the IBA Program and its partners.

Pahranagat NWR is an oasis in southern Nevada. The refuge encompasses a 10-mile stretch of Pahranagat Valley and associated desert uplands. The White River, an ancient perennial stream which was a tributary of the Colorado River, flowed through the Pahranagat Valley from the north. It established a well-defined but relatively narrow flood plain. The river bed is dry for many miles upstream and downstream from Pahranagat Valley, but there is water in the valley that comes from large, thermal springs along the flood plain. This spring water is impounded in the refuge's Upper Lake and North Marsh and is released to create conditions that enhance the growth of wildlife food plants and supplement lakes, marshes, and grasslands south of the refuge headquarters.

Key Pittman WMA includes two small lakes near the town of Hiko. The town and the lakes are located in a broad valley with mountain ranges on both sides. In the bottom of the valley, farm fields attract a variety of waterfowl, shorebirds, cranes, hawks, and other birds.

Nesbitt Lake, the northern-most of the two lakes, is a broad, moderately deep lake with open water year-round. Frenchy Lake, the southern lake, is broad and very shallow, with open water only during some years. When it is wet, an extensive marsh surrounds almost the entire lake. (Boone 2004)

Land uses within the Pahranagat Valley Complex include agriculture, tourism and recreation, conservation, low density development, and hunting.

Birds

Pahranagat NWR hosts thousands of migratory birds each year, and more than 230 different species of birds have been recorded at the refuge. Bird abundance and diversity is highest during spring and fall migrations when large numbers of songbirds, waterfowl, shorebirds, and raptors converge. Common ducks are Northern Pintail, Cinnamon Teal, Mallard, and Redhead. Great Blue Herons are found near lakes while Black-necked Stilts and American Avocets feed in shallow water. Greater Sandhill Cranes can be seen February-March and again October-November as they migrate between nesting and wintering areas. Red-tailed Hawks, Northern Harriers, Cooper's Hawks, and American Kestrels are most abundant during winter months and both Bald Eagles and Golden Eagles are winter visitors. Cottonwood-willow habitat provides nesting habitat for warblers, orioles, flycatchers, and finches. The open fields attract shrikes, meadowlarks, blackbirds, and mourning doves. The uplands are home to Gambel's Quail, Greater Roadrunners, and various species of sparrows. (U.S. Fish and Wildlife Service 2004c)

The lakes at Key Pittman WMA provide habitat for waterfowl, wading birds, shorebirds, pelicans, cranes, and hawks. During migration, swallows, nighthawks, flycatchers, and warblers use the area as a stopover. During summer, the WMA provides nesting sites for Southwestern Willow Flycatchers and Yellow-billed Cuckoos. (Boone 2004) Other key species in this IBA include Bald Eagle, Blue Grosbeak, Clapper Rail, and Yellow Warbler.

Key species used to identify the Pahranagat Valley Complex IBA and the criteria met by the site. Criteria codes are discussed in Appendix II.						
Species	Year	Season	Min	Max	Units	Confirmed
Northern Pintail	1997	migration	--	18,000	individuals	NV3g, NV3a
Canvasback	1997	migration	--	5,000	individuals	NV3g, NV3a
Sandhill Crane	1998	migration	--	400	individuals	NV1, NV3g
Willow Flycatcher	2001	breeding	--	54	adults	NV1, NV3g

Conservation Issues

The presence of water makes conditions ripe for invasive plant species. Tamarisk, Russian olive, and annual grasses are but a few of the threats that land managers battle. Pahranagat Valley is also threatened by over-exploitation of groundwater resources to satisfy Las Vegas' needs.

Visiting the Site

Primary places for viewing wildlife are at the lakes described in the text above. Spring and fall migration are the best viewing times, though a winter visit can also yield some interesting finds. Rarities occasionally show up here and reward the attentive birdwatcher.

Pyramid Lake

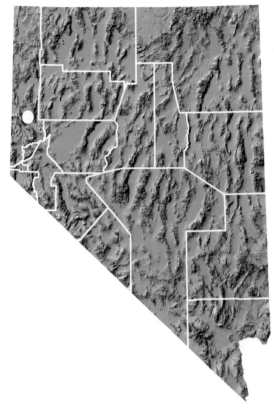

Area: 46,119 ha
UTM Easting: 281673
UTM Northing: 4435672

Description

Pyramid Lake sits in a basin once occupied by the much larger Pleistocene-era Lake Lahontan. Several ancient beach lines marking prehistoric lake levels are visible within the basin. The three surrounding mountain ranges (Virginia Mountains, Pah Rah Range, Lake Range) are classic basin and range, block fault uplift mountains. The Truckee River, the major tributary to the lake, provides approximately 500,000 acre-feet of inflow each year, depending on climate and upstream agricultural, municipal, and industrial diversions. Plant communities surrounding the lake are dominated by desert shrub and also include limited riparian and wetland habitats.

Two prominent islands are visible in the lake. Pyramid Island is steep, arid, and relatively small. Anaho Island is larger and lower in profile and supports extensive nesting colonies of American White Pelicans. Peregrine Falcons historically nested on the island as well. The island constitutes the entire extent of the Anaho Island NWR. The refuge was established by President Woodrow Wilson in 1913 as a sanctuary for colonial nesting birds. Anaho Island is a part of the Pyramid Lake Paiute Indian Reservation, but is managed by the U.S. Fish and Wildlife Service under an agreement with the Tribe. (U.S. Fish and Wildlife Service 2004d) Land uses at the IBA include fishing, conservation, research, recreation and tourism, and water management.

Birds

Anaho Island supports one of the largest breeding colonies of American White Pelicans in the western United States. In recent years, between 8,000 and 10,000 pelicans have returned to Anaho Island during the spring from their wintering areas in southern California and Baja California, Mexico. These fish-eating birds rely on the spring spawning runs of Pyramid Lake fish as well as the numerous shallow lakes and wetlands within 70 miles of the island, primarily in the Lahontan Valley and Stillwater NWR. The island also provides nesting habitat for Double-crested Cormorants, California Gulls, Great Blue Herons, Black-crowned Night Herons, and occasionally Caspian Terns. (U.S. Fish and Wildlife Service 2004d)

The lake as a whole provides migration stopover opportunities for significant numbers of waterbirds. Large numbers of Clark's and Western Grebes, Eared Grebes, American White Pelicans, and numerous species of ducks pass through in migration.

Other key species at the site include Eared Grebe, Ruddy Duck, Redhead, Bufflehead, American Coot, Common Merganser, and Common Loon. Of general interest is the fact that Pyramid Lake attracts pelagic species, and the occasional errant Yellow-billed Loon, jaeger, scoter, or unusual gull shows up here often enough to make this a birding destination.

Key species used to identify the Pyramid Lake IBA and the criteria met by the site. Proposed criteria await the availability of additional data prior to evaluation by the Nevada IBA TAC. Criteria codes are discussed in Appendix II.

Species	Year	Season	Min	Max	Units	Proposed	Confirmed
Clark's/Western Grebe	2000	migration	--	8,518	individuals	NV3g	NV3a
American White Pelican	1999	breeding	--	20,000	adults only		NV1, NV3g, NV3gv
Great Blue Heron	1999	breeding	--	100	adults only		NV3e
California Gull	1999	breeding	--	5,500	adults only	NV3g	NV3gv

An American Birding Association tour visits Pyramid Lake IBA

Conservation Issues

Water supply is forever a concern in Great Basin aquatic systems. As a terminal water body, the lake is at the end of the line for receiving whatever water is not withdrawn to meet upstream permitted withdrawals. The Pyramid Lake Paiute have water rights dedicated to the lake, and there is certainly long-term interest in maintaining the lake's fishery. Nonetheless, in low-water years getting adequate water to the lake can be problematic and the lake level has dropped gradually since the early 1900s. A variety of agencies and organizations are working to secure more reliable water delivery.

There is an interesting and complex relationship between the American White Pelicans at Anaho Island and the Endangered Cui ui chub, a Pyramid Lake endemic upon which the pelican relies for part of its forage. Managing the recovery and restoration of the Cui ui while also maintaining one of the most important breeding populations of American White Pelicans is a delicate balancing act.

Visiting the Site

The entire area lies on Pyramid Lake Paiute Tribal Lands and a permit is required for each vehicle visiting the area. A permit is available from Sutcliffe Marina or the convenience store in Nixon. The best places for bird watching lie along the west shore and at the southern end of Pyramid Lake. Anaho Island NWR is closed to visitors to avoid disturbing this critical nesting area. To the north of Sutcliffe, an area known as The Willows is a great site for migrant songbirds. Sutcliffe Marina and several pull-outs along NV 446 south of the marina are all great places for scanning the lake for resting birds. At the south end of the lake, scan the delta area for migrating shorebirds.

American White Pelicans at Anaho Island (© Bob Goodman)

Ruby Lake

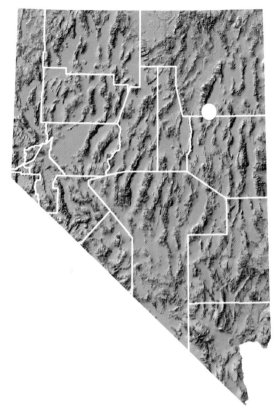

Area: 15,697 ha
UTM Easting: 630635
UTM Northing: 4448660

Description

The Ruby Lake IBA is comprised principally of Ruby Lake NWR, which is located in a closed basin at the southern end of Ruby Valley in northeastern Nevada. The refuge consists of a high quality marsh bordered by meadows, grasslands, shrub steppe, and playa. The 20,000-acre seasonal and permanent marsh is a mosaic of bullrush, open water, and islands. The refuge is 18 miles long and 3 miles wide at its widest point. Over 200 springs flow into the marsh. The primary purposes of the area are as a refuge and breeding ground for migratory birds and other wildlife and as an inviolate sanctuary. The refuge is one of the most important areas for wildlife in the Great Basin. Land uses within the Ruby Lake IBA include conservation, hunting, rangeland, and tourism and recreation.

Birds

The refuge supports over 225 species of birds and numerous priority bird species including Greater Sage-Grouse and several species of warblers. The area's most important function is a nesting, resting, and wintering area for waterbirds. The refuge becomes increasingly vital during drought periods as other areas become dry. The breeding Canvasback population is the largest west of the Mississippi River (excluding Alaska) and the highest concentration of nesting Canvasbacks in the world. Average spring population of waterfowl is 8,181, fall mean population is 16,545 swans, geese, and ducks. Average breeding population of swans, geese, and ducks is 3,260 pairs with an average production of 6,324. The IBA supports the highest nesting density of Greater Sandhill Crane in northeastern Nevada and, therefore, probably the entire state.

Species used to identify the Ruby Lake IBA and the criteria met by the site. Proposed criteria await evaluation by the National Technical Committee. Criteria codes are discussed in Appendices II and III.

Species	Year	Season	Min	Max	Units	Proposed	Confirmed
White-faced Ibis	1996	breeding	--	468	individuals		NV1, NV3g
Ruddy Duck	1997	migration	--	480	individuals		NV3a
Trumpeter Swan	1997	all	--	59	individuals	B1	NV3a
Canada Goose	1997	migration	--	360	individuals		NV3a
Gadwall	1997	migration	--	4,120	individuals		NV3a
American Wigeon	1997	migration	--	1,205	individuals		NV3a
Mallard	1997	migration	--	2,718	individuals		NV3a
Cinnamon Teal	1997	migration	--	1,542	individuals		NV3a
Northern Shoveler	1997	migration	--	2,264	individuals		NV3a
Northern Pintail	1997	migration	--	5,427	individuals		NV3a
Green-winged Teal	1997	migration	--	4,197	individuals		NV3a
Canvasback	2001	breeding	520	--	breeding pairs		NV3g, NV3a
Canvasback	1997	migration	--	1,644	individuals		NV3a
Redhead	1997	migration	--	1,151	individuals		NV3a
Ring-necked Duck	1997	migration	--	168	individuals		NV3a
Lesser Scaup	1997	migration	--	569	individuals		NV3a
Sandhill Crane	2003	breeding	--	45	individuals		NV1,NV3g
American Coot	1997	migration	--	7,609	individuals		NV3a
Forster's Tern	2003	breeding	--	168	individuals		NV1, NV3gv
Black Tern	2001	breeding	--	300	individuals		NV1, NV3g, NV3gv

Conservation Issues

At the refuge a high density of coyotes impact sandhill crane and waterfowl production. There is no current plan in place to address this issue. Introduced game fish are impacting the ecology of natural systems and in turn impacting waterfowl production. Additional information is needed before this problem can be addressed. Recreational use of the refuge creates disturbance to birds, though recreation is regulated and the degree of disturbance and impacts is unknown. Grasslands are being restored through the use of prescribed fire (a beneficial action), and invading cattails and bulrush are being treated to reduce emergent vegetation and maintain open water.

Visiting the Site

Ruby Lake NWR welcomes visitors. A system of roads follows the network of dykes used to control water at the refuge, offering bird watchers an excellent means for accessing the marshes and ponds. A stand of trees around refuge headquarters is also worth checking for songbirds.

Black Tern (© Bob Goodman)

94

Ruby Mountains

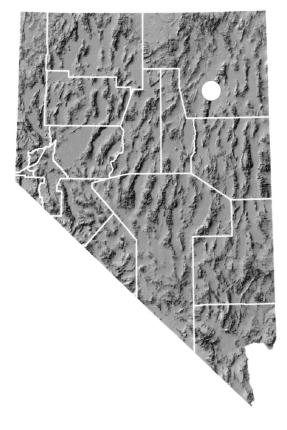

Area: 127,327 ha
UTM Easting: 635760
UTM Northing: 4492471

Description

Nevada's Ruby Mountains invite endless comparison to better known landscapes. The range is collectively known as Nevada's Alps, and Lamoille Canyon as Nevada's Yosemite. Comparisons aside, superlatives are warranted. To those who have visited this cordillera the name of the Ruby Mountains will evoke an image of high, multi-faceted, granite peaks soaring above lush green meadows and sparkling sapphire blue lakes. Long and narrow, the Rubies stretch 100 miles and seldom exceed 10 miles in width. Glaciers scoured the northern end of the Rubies during the last ice age, creating the classically U-shaped Lamoille Canyon. Hanging valleys, towering summits, and year-round snowfields characterize the range. The U.S. Congress designated the Ruby Mountains Wilderness Area in 1989; the wilderness area now encompasses 36,422 ha.

South of Lamoille Canyon lie 7 miles of lake basins and meadows before the terrain south of Furlong Lake turns into a narrow, grassy ridge that runs 20 miles to the Overland Lake basin. The Rubies contain 10 peaks above 10,000 feet (including Ruby Dome at 11,387 feet) and more than two dozen alpine lakes, rare treats in this arid state.

Habitat in the Ruby Mountains IBA varies considerably with altitude. At lower elevations sagebrush shrublands dominate. At higher elevations montane shrublands and parklands intersperse with piñon-juniper forests, mixed conifer forests, and aspens. Cliffs are abundant in this dramatic landscape, and a few permanent snow fields persist throughout the year.

Land uses include nature and wildlife conservation, wilderness, hunting and fishing, various forms of recreation and tourism, summer rangeland, and water supply.

Birds

The Ruby Mountains IBA is one of the few sites in Nevada that has both the high altitude habitat *and* the associated bird species. The Rubies are particularly noteworthy for rosy finches, and all three species have been recorded in the area over the course of a year (Black Rosy-Finch is a breeder here, Gray-crowned Rosy-Finch a possible breeder; Brown-capped Rosy Finch also winters in the area). The Rubies remain wild terrain and support montane habitats in good condition.

Of general ornithological interest are the Himalayan Snowcocks and Hungarian Partridges that have been introduced and are doing well. The Himalayan Snowcock occurs nowhere else in North America, and its presence attracts life listers and hunters alike.

Species used to identify the Ruby Mountains IBA and the criteria met by the site. Proposed criteria await review by the National Technical Committee. Codes for criteria are discussed in Appendices II and III.

Species	Year	Season	Pairs/km^{2*} Min	Max	Proposed	Confirmed
MacGillivray's Warbler	2000	breeding	1	>44		NV1
Orange-crowned Warbler	2000	breeding	1	43		NV1
Wilson's Warbler	2000	breeding	1	4		NV1
Red-naped Sapsucker	2000	breeding	0	43		NV1
Lewis's Woodpecker	2000	breeding	1	43		NV1
Vesper Sparrow	1998	breeding	1	4		NV1
Sage Thrasher	1998	breeding	1	43		NV1
Northern Goshawk	2000	breeding	0	<1		NV1, NV2
Gray Flycatcher	1998	breeding	0	4		NV1
Prairie Falcon	1998	breeding	0	<1		NV1
Black Rosy-Finch	2000	breeding	1	4	B1	NV1, NV2

*Density estimated in appropriate habitat and in the appropriate season.

Conservation Issues

As with other Forest Service lands, there is a need for specific management guidelines that regulate ORV use for the Ruby Mountains. Disturbance to birds attributable to this source extends to snowmobiles in winter. Some members of the IBA Technical Advisory Committee also identified potential harassment of Himalayan Snowcock and possibly other species by birders using helicopters to access the remote terrain where this species occurs. Although it seems unlikely that this occurs on any regular basis, it may be worth monitoring this small user group to assure that the activity does not have a negative impact on the resource.

Grazing has been managed with varying success, depending on allotment. The Forest Service is working with lease holders and trying to build community support for better oversight of range use and better voluntary self-regulation. Some drainages may need fencing, bank stabilization, and some form of change in the grazing management. More information is needed on this concern.

Ruby Mountains rise above the Humboldt River

Visiting the Site

The Ruby Mountains offer many opportunities for exploration, whether from a vehicle or by foot, and from a few hours to weeks. Lamoille Canyon is one of the most popular destinations, and it is accessible by car and offers many pullouts and opportunities for short hikes or explorations. Longer trails depart from various points in Lamoille Canyon. Harrison Pass to the south of Lamoille Canyon also offers pullouts and short hikes. A search for the Himalayan Snowcock can be an epic undertaking. One of the more reliable sites for this species is the talus slopes above Island Lake, and the trailhead for this destination lies at the top of Lamoille Canyon.

Sheep Range

Area: 24,179 ha
UTM Easting: 662478
UTM Northing: 4060794

Description

The Sheep Range IBA is located on the eastern edge of the Desert National Wildlife Range (NWR). The Desert NWR was established May 20, 1936, and encompasses 1.5 million acres of the diverse Mojave Desert in southern Nevada; it is the largest NWR in the lower 48 states. The NWR contains 6 major mountain ranges, the highest rising from 2,500-foot valleys to nearly 10,000 feet. Annual rainfall ranges from less than 4 inches on the valley floors to over 15 inches on the highest peaks.

Perpetuating the desert bighorn sheep and its habitat is the primary objective of the NWR. The range improves bighorn habitats by developing new water sources and maintaining and improving existing sources.

Plant communities and wildlife found on the range vary with altitude and climate. The desert shrub community, composed of creosote bush and white bursage, dominates the hottest, lowest elevations of Desert NWR. Mojave yucca and cactus become abundant above the valley floor; these communities are below the IBA boundary. At the upper edge of the desert shrub communities, between approximately 4,200 feet and 6,000 feet, black-brush and Joshua tree are dominant. Above 6,000 feet desert woodlands, composed of single-leaf piñon, Utah juniper, and big sagebrush are extant. The coniferous forest communities begin around 7,000 feet. From 7,000 to 9,000 ponderosa pine and white fir are the dominant trees. Near 10,000 feet, where the growing seasons are the shortest, the only trees surviving are bristlecone pines.

Numerous recreational opportunities are available on the range. Camping, hiking, backpacking, and horseback riding are all popular activities enjoyed by refuge visitors. Limited hunting for bighorn sheep is permitted. Bird watching is also a popular activity, with a bird list available at the range or online. An active volunteer program provides additional opportunities at the refuge. (U.S. Fish

Flammulated Owl (© Bob Goodman)

and Wildlife Service 2004e). Land uses within the Sheep Range IBA include conservation and research, and tourism and recreation.

Birds

The Sheep Range appears to be the northern limit for Mexican Whip-poor-wills, seven of which were located within the IBA in July 1997. This is also the only place they are known to occur in the state. In the arid mountains of southern Nevada, this area provides three different life zones, from upper Sonoran to Canadian zones, providing great habitat diversity for birds. Small seeps and springs provide valuable surface water for birds. Other species of note include Red-naped Sapsucker, Western Bluebird, and Red Crossbill.

Species used to identify the Sheep Range IBA and the criteria met by the site. Criterion NV1 covers species of conservation concern in Nevada.

Species	Year	Season	pairs/km²*		Confirmed
			Min	Max	
Flammulated Owl	2000	breeding	1	4	NV1
Gray Flycatcher	2000	breeding	1	43	NV1
Black-throated Gray Warbler	2000	breeding	1	43	NV1
Grace's Warbler	2000	breeding	0	4	NV1

*Density estimated in appropriate habitat and in the appropriate season.

Conservation Issues

As a part of the National Wildlife Refuge System, priority for management of the Sheep Range is given to sustaining its wildlife values. As such, this IBA appears to be fairly secure from threats. Invasive plants are a low-level threat that warrants monitoring to assure they do not become a larger issue.

Visiting the Site

The Sheep Range constitutes one of many remote and isolated sites in Nevada. One of the more popular access points for the few visitors who make it in each year is called Hidden Forest, which lies on the west side of the range. Hidden Forest Trail is accessible from Alamo Road, just north of Corn Creek. Birding along this trail is best accomplished through an overnight visit.

Sheldon National Wildlife Refuge

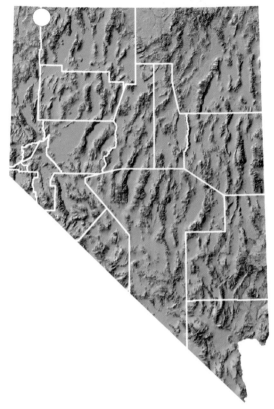

Area: 236,894 ha
UTM Easting: 316177
UTM Northing: 4631880

Description

The National Audubon Society and the Sheldon NWR have an interesting history together. The refuge's genesis was the result of fundraising and political persuasion spearheaded by Thomas Gilbert Pearson, a past president of the National Audubon Society (then called the National Association of Audubon Societies). For the princely sum of 7,500 dollars, Pearson acquired possession on behalf of Audubon of the 380-acre Last Chance Ranch on December 24, 1927, and this became the nucleus of the refuge (Pearson 1937). Pearson then approached Kermit Roosevelt, Secretary of the Boone and Crockett Club, who agreed to join forces with Pearson and Audubon and work collaboratively to acquire numerous parcels of private land. Nevada was open to homesteading in those days so President Hoover withdrew from settlement 30,720 acres near and adjacent to the growing refuge. On January 26, 1931, the area was declared by Executive Order to be the Charles Sheldon Wild Life Refuge; it was named after a prominent sportsman who was both a past president of Boone and Crockett and the National Audubon Society. Audubon maintained warden service on the refuge for the first four-and-a-half years of its existence.

The original refuge established in 1931 encompassed just over 34,000 acres. Additional adjacent lands were set aside in 1936 as the Charles Sheldon Antelope Range, or Game Range, boasting over 540,000 acres. The two areas were combined to form what is now the Sheldon NWR under the administration of the U.S. Fish and Wildlife Service. The broad mission of the National Wildlife Refuge system has been translated into a specific refuge objective for Sheldon–to manage the refuge as a representative area of high-desert habitat for optimum populations of native plants and wildlife.

The refuge is primarily high, semi-desert country typical of the Columbia Plateau region, characterized by volcanic bedrock, large tablelands and rolling hills. Surface water supplies are limited, usually to seeps and springs, though some impoundments exist. Annual precipitation averages less than 13 inches in the western portions of the refuge and decreases to 6 inches in the eastern part of the range. The plateau is interrupted by narrow valleys and canyons bordered by precipitous rocky rims. Elevations range from 4,500 to 7,600 feet.

Sandhill Crane (© Richard S. Barrett)

Vegetation is dominated by communities of big sagebrush, low sagebrush, rabbitbrush, and bitterbrush. Meadow vegetation (grasses and forbs) and riparian vegetation (aspens and willows) are limited to areas around the few water sources found on the refuge. Mountain mahogany and western juniper stands are found on higher elevations. Other important habitats include alkaline lakes, marshes, grassy spring-fed meadows, greasewood flats, juniper covered uplands, and aspen stands in the more secluded canyon areas. Each of these habitats supports its own particular suite of bird species. (Nevada Wildlife Federation 2004)

Range quality in the Sheldon suffered from decades of mismanaged grazing. Allotments have been closed and the area has recovered to the extent that it now represents one of the best examples of sagebrush-steppe habitat in the Great Basin. As such, the refuge is a significant area for the maintenance of sagebrush obligates, including Greater Sage-Grouse, Sage Thrasher, and Sage Sparrow. Ongoing studies indicate significant use of the refuge by a range of birds (Earnst 2002), though sagebrush-steppe associated species are certainly the most extensively represented.

Land use in this IBA is established by the mission and management focus of the refuge and includes conservation and research, tourism and recreation, and hunting and fishing.

Birds

This landscape constitutes one of the best remaining examples of an intact desert shrub community in Nevada. Although altered through decades of grazing, the ecosystem has rebounded remarkably with the removal of cows. Management direction is towards habitat restoration and enhancement. Sagebrush obligates are the noteworthy species.

Species used to identify the Sheldon NWR IBA and the criteria met by the site. Proposed criteria await evaluation by the National Technical Committee (A1) or the Nevada IBA TAC pending availability of additional data. Criteria codes are discussed in Appendices II and III.

Species	Year	Season	Min	Max	Units	Proposed	Confirmed
Greater Sage-Grouse	2001	breeding	1,600	2,500	adults	A1	NV1, NV3g
Gray Flycatcher	2000	breeding	1	45	pairs/km^{2*}	NV3g	NV1
Sage Thrasher	2000	breeding	1	45	pairs/km^{2*}	NV3g	NV1
Vesper Sparrow	2000	breeding	1	45	pairs/km^{2*}	NV3g	NV1
Sage Sparrow	2000	breeding	1	45	pairs/km^{2*}	NV3g	NV1

*Density estimated in appropriate habitat and in the appropriate season.

Conservation Issues

Maintenance of this sagebrush-steppe landscape is complicated by the duality of wildfires. On the one hand, fires are a natural part of the regenerative cycle that encourages habitat heterogeneity, although natural fires appear to have occurred on 75 to 100 year cycles. With the introduction of cheatgrass and other annual weedy species, fires encourage the establishment of invasive species, which in turn drastically shortens fire recurrence. These shorter intervals, sometimes as short as 3-5 years, do not permit the re-establishment of native shrubs and as a result annual grasses (and other weeds) begin to dominate the landscape. Management at Sheldon includes conducting prescribed burns and rehabilitation efforts for wildfires in an effort to meet the needs of the landscape without encouraging weeds. Other management issues at Sheldon include a burgeoning wild horse population, issues associated with ORV use, erosion, and expansion of juniper into shrub communities.

Visiting the Site

The Sheldon NWR is a huge landscape but there are numerous places that visitors can get acquainted with the avifauna. There are several impoundments along US 140 that are worth exploring, and a drive through this area should include stops at Big Spring Reservoir and Catnip Reservoir. The Virgin Valley Ranch Road and ponds along this route are worth a morning's birding. Cottonwood Creek Canyon is also an excellent destination, though four-wheel drive is essential.

The sagebrush ocean, Sheldon National Wildlife Refuge

Spring Mountains

Area: 108,768 ha
UTM Easting: 617550
UTM Northing: 4016028

Description

The majority of this IBA is comprised of the Spring Mountains National Recreation Area, administered by the Forest Service. The Spring Mountains of southern Nevada are located near the southernmost border with California. Pahrump Valley and the Amargosa River basin lie to the west and Las Vegas Valley, draining to the Colorado River, lies to the east. The Spring Mountains are probably the most biologically diverse of all Nevada's mountain ranges. This diversity is reflected by the 37 tree species known from the range, more than any other mountain range in Nevada. There are probably more than 1,000 plant species in the Spring Mountains, and thus it possesses about one third of the entire Nevada flora, including many endemic species.

The vegetation series in the Spring Mountains begins at its lowest slopes with creosote bush -white bursage shrublands of the Lower Mojavean Zone. As elevation increases, the vegetation community phases into blackbrush shrublands, then into piñon-juniper woodlands. Curlleaf mahogany becomes a component of this forest at its higher elevations. Above the pygmy forest, the montane zone contains large woodlands of mountain mahogany, mixed conifer forests consisting of ponderosa pine and white fir. At slightly higher elevations, these forests also include limber pine, bristlecone pine in the overstory, and common juniper in the understory. Small aspen stands occur on north and east aspects in this zone. A tiny alpine zone occurs on Charleston Peak. Thus, the Spring Mountains contain all the vegetation zones in Nevada except for the sagebrush and absolute desert zones. (Biological Resources Research Center 2004)

Land uses within this IBA are dictated by the management of the Spring Mountains National Recreation Area. Uses include conservation and research, wilderness, tourism and recreation, and limited urban-suburban development.

Birds

The bird community of the Spring Mountains is in many ways its least unique feature–the noteworthy endemism belongs to other, less mobile flora and fauna. Nonetheless, the area is remarkable for the type of habitats it provides for birds, many of which are otherwise largely absent from the Mojave Desert. Flammulated Owls breed in the coniferous forests, constituting the highest recorded density of breeding Flammulated Owls in Nevada. Most of the species characterizing this IBA are associated with the conifer forests. Significant numbers of Rufous Hummingbirds migrate through the Spring Mountains. A weak raptor migration passes down the range in fall and is most visible in Potosi Pass.

Species used to identify the Spring Mountains IBA and the criteria met by the site. Proposed criteria await additional data prior to review by the Nevada IBA TAC. Criteria codes are discussed in Appendix II.

Species	Year	Season	Min	Max	Units	Proposed	Confirmed
Northern Goshawk	2000	breeding	0	<1	pairs/km^{2*}		NV1
Gray Vireo	2002	breeding	20	-	individuals		NV1
Wilson's Warbler	2002	migration	100	-	individuals		NV1
Flammulated Owl	2002	breeding	15	-	pairs	NV3g	NV1
Red-naped Sapsucker	1999	breeding	0	<1	pairs/km^{2*}		NV1
Olive-sided Flycatcher	2000	breeding	0	<1	pairs/km^{2*}		NV1
Willow Flycatcher	2002	migration	--	30	individuals		NV1
Gray Flycatcher	2000	breeding	1	4	pairs/km^{2*}		NV1
Ash-throated Flycatcher	2002	breeding	30	--	individuals		NV1
Virginia's Warbler	2000	breeding	1	4	pairs/km^{2*}		NV1
Black-throated Gray Warbler	2000	breeding	1	4	pairs/km^{2*}		NV1
Grace's Warbler	2000	breeding	1	4	pairs/km^{2*}		NV1
MacGillivray's Warbler	2000	breeding	0	1	pairs/km^{2*}		NV1
Cooper's Hawk	2000	breeding	0	1	pairs/km^{2*}		NV1
Orange-crowned Warbler	2000	breeding	0	1	pairs/km^{2*}		NV1
Pinyon Jay	2000	breeding	1	4	pairs/km^{2*}		NV1
Western Bluebird	2000	breeding	1	4	pairs/km^{2*}		NV1

*Density estimated in appropriate habitat and in the appropriate season.

Conservation Issues

Moderate threats to this area include invasive plants and excessive demand for recreation opportunities. With its proximity to Las Vegas, the Spring Mountains are a popular destination for those wishing to escape the summer heat of the desert. Traffic can be heavy, especially on weekends. The Forest Service has recently been working to establish a travel plan and better define access for all user groups.

Visiting the Site

Kyle and Lee Canyons are popular Spring Mountains access points. The Forest Service maintains an extensive trail network that accesses more remote terrain.

Swan Lake

Area: 474 ha
UTM Easting: 256059
UTM Northing: 4393291

Description

Swan Lake is an historic wetland with evidence of prehistoric use by the Washoe Tribe. The area consists of permanent wetlands that range from 50-100 acres during drought conditions to 1,000 acres during high water cycles. Emergent vegetation of cattails and two species of bulrush characterize the wetlands, with uplands of sage and native grasses. Tall whitetop has invaded some of the area. Ownership is 90 percent public land (BLM, Washoe County, Nevada Military) with the remaining area comprised of private in-holdings. Effort has been made in recent years to acquire private parcels from willing sellers using Land and Water Conservation Funds.

Swan Lake Nature Study Area is an active interpretive site with kiosks, reader boards, a boardwalk in the marsh, bus parking, and trails. It is being managed by the Washoe County Parks and Recreation Department through guidelines drawn up by eight cooperating entities, including the Lahontan Audubon Society.

The Lemmon Valley Sewage Treatment Facility's system of ponds are immediately adjacent to the lake and provide nesting, feeding, and migratory resting for significant bird populations, especially when the lake is frozen in winter months, or during drought conditions.

Birds

Swan Lake serves as an important year-round site for birds. There are resident birds that nest and raise broods here. Other birds are winter residents, coming after raising their broods in the more northern lands and include the namesake Tundra Swans. Still other species depend on Swan Lake for the stopover needs of migration, staying a few days to a few weeks. These include large numbers of shorebirds and wading birds.

As the Reno-Sparks area continues to have one of the fastest growing populations in the West, the preservation of a natural wetland system becomes ever more important for the avian population that depends on its water and vegetation for survival.

Species	Year	Season	Min	Max	Units	Confirmed
Black-necked Stilt	2003	migration	100	500	individuals	NV1
American Avocet	2003	migration	100	500	individuals	NV1
American Avocet	2003	breeding	40	50	individuals	NV1
White-faced Ibis	2003	breeding	30	40	individuals	NV1
Burrowing Owl	2003	breeding	6	10	individuals	NV1
Tundra Swan	2002	winter	400	1,500	individuals	NV3a
Waterfowl (18+ species)	1999	winter	1,000	5,000	individuals	NV3a

Species used to identify the Swan Lake IBA and the criteria met by the site. Criteria codes are discussed in Appendix II.

Conservation Issues

Some surface water and support of emergent marsh vegetation is guaranteed to Swan Lake under an agreement to receive 490 acre-feet of effluent from the Stead Sewage Treatment Plant. There is some threat to natural in-flow sources by off-site commercial and residential development. Tall whitetop control is being implemented on a trial basis on the military portion of the site. Traditional ORV use of the area is decreasing due to public education and site development for education. The wetland area is largely in natural condition, but surrounding uplands need Best Management Plans, and the inflow at Horse Ravine needs stabilization.

Visiting the Site

Swan Lake has two easily accessed areas for a good bird watching experience. There is a boardwalk into the permanent marsh off of Lear Boulevard. The other access point is at the settling ponds at the end of Patricia Street.

Swan Lake (© Bob Goodman)

Toiyabe Range

Area: 189,541 ha
UTM Easting: 474913
UTM Northing: 4316240

Description

Most of this large landscape is managed under the jurisdiction of the Humboldt-Toiyabe National Forest. The entire Toiyabe Range (a significant portion is included in the IBA) is 126 miles long, with 50 contiguous miles where the center spine never drops below 10,000 feet. Montane shrub and piñon-juniper communities are interspersed with mountain mahogany, aspen and limber pine groves. The highest elevations are covered by low sagebrush and an alpine flora of fewer than 50 species.

The range is wet by Great Basin standards, with streams like the North and South Twin rivers, Peavine Creek, Stewart Creek, Reese River, Big Creek, and Kingston Creek, all with lush riparian areas and abundant shrubs and trees including chokecherry, elderberry, red osier dogwood, cottonwood, aspen, and water birch. The IBA includes a portion of the Arc Dome Wilderness Area, the largest in the state at 115,000 acres. The Arc Dome crest is at 11,788 feet, the tenth highest summit in Nevada.

The western boundary of this IBA includes a portion of the Reese River Valley where the river exits the range. This area is important to the resident Greater Sage-Grouse population, providing key wintering habitat and lek sites.

Located in central Nevada, the range is about as far from population centers as one can get in Nevada, though it was not always so. Austin, located above the northern border of this IBA, sprang into being after the discovery of silver at that spot in 1862, and in its heyday became a substantial city of 10,000 people. From Austin, prospectors fanned out to open many other important mining camps throughout the Toiyabe Range. Today, evidence of mining within the IBA is relatively small-scale and of a historic nature. An exception is an open pit operation on the west-central side of the IBA that is being reclaimed.

Land uses within the Toiyabe Range IBA include conservation and research, wilderness, rangeland, hunting and fishing, tourism and recreation, and mineral extraction.

Birds

The site supports one of the larger Greater Sage-Grouse populations in the state, with an interesting migration pattern that sees them using the upper elevations of the range in summer and moving down to the Reese River Valley in winter. The site also contains extensive mountain shrub and the more rare montane parkland habitat types, and the associated bird species of concern.

Species used to identify the Toiyabe Range IBA and the criteria met by the site. Proposed criteria await evaluation by the National Technical Committee. Codes for criteria are discussed in Appendices II and III.

Species	Year	Season	Min	Max	Units	Proposed	Confirmed
Greater Sage-Grouse	2002	breeding	--	1,500	adults	A1	NV1, NV3g
Pinyon Jay	2000	breeding	1	>44	pairs/km^{2}*	A1	NV1, NV3g
Sage Thrasher	1997	breeding	1	4	pairs/km^{2}*		NV1
Juniper Titmouse	2000	breeding	1	4	pairs/km^{2}*		NV1
Gray Flycatcher	2000	breeding	0	43	pairs/km^{2}*		NV1
Ash-throated Flycatcher	2000	breeding	0	4	pairs/km^{2}*		NV1
Willow Flycatcher	1997	breeding	0	<1	pairs/km^{2}*		NV1
Wilson's Warbler	1997	breeding	1	4	pairs/km^{2}*		NV1
Orange-crowned Warbler	1997	breeding	1	4	pairs/km^{2}*		NV1
Black-throated Gray Warbler	2000	breeding	1	>44	pairs/km^{2}*		NV1
Sage Sparrow	1998	breeding	1	4	pairs/km^{2}*		NV1

*Densities are calculated based on appropriate habitats, not the entire landscape.

More than 17 Nevada Partners in Flight priority species utilize this landscape for various parts of their life histories. While this IBA is critical for Greater Sage-Grouse, it also is likely to be some of the best habitat in the state for Pinyon Jays. This species is highly mobile and somewhat irruptive in its distribution, but the ranges of Central Nevada (including the Toiyabe, Toquima, and Monitor ranges) likely form the core of Pinyon Jay populations in Nevada. Other Partners in Flight species in this landscape include Black-throated Gray Warbler, Juniper Titmouse, Gray Flycatcher, Wilson's Warbler, Sage Thrasher, Orange-crowned Warbler, Ash-throated Flycatcher, and Sage Sparrow.

Conservation Issues

As with nearly all landscapes in Nevada, the Toiyabe Range has experienced a range of vegetation-altering activities. The interaction between fire and grazing has altered some portions of the landscape. Consequently, cheatgrass is present, though generally only problematic in some burns.

To help mitigate landscape-level vegetation conversion, fire-fuels management is essential, as is a rapid follow-up to a fire event. In many cases, particularly at lower elevations, native re-seeding of burned landscapes may be critical to control the spread of cheatgrass.

The riparian zones vary in quality from excellent to degraded. Cattle tend to congregate in the cool, wet riparian areas and disproportionately impact this

Aspens and willows along the Reese River, Toiyabe Range IBA

habitat type. Some perennial stream stretches in the Toiyabes have been fenced to regulate access. This strategy is successful depending on whether fences are maintained and gates are closed. Areas that are not fenced can be badly degraded. Efforts to work with leasees to better manage grazing are ongoing.

As remote as the range is, it is not beyond the reach of ORV enthusiasts. Recently, as a result of increased regulation at Sand Mountain, ORV use has shifted towards the largely unregulated Toiyabe Range. The Forest Service is working to evaluate their travel management plan and determine where ORV use is appropriate in an effort to reduce resource damage from this source.

Visiting the Site

Kingston and Big Creek Canyons are two of the more accessible and well watered areas. A trip through this area (the two canyons connect) by car, with numerous stops, is worthwhile. Other options for the more intrepid include backpacking or horse packing into one of the perennial drainages, such as the Reese River or San Juan Creek.

Virgin River

Area: 6,249 ha
UTM Easting: 744273
UTM Northing: 4058149

Description

The lower Virgin River from just north of Mesquite to the Overton Arm is located in extreme southern Nevada within the northeast portion of Clark County. The riparian habitat of the river is a mixture of lowland riparian vegetation. The riparian vegetation includes coyote and Gooding's willow, arrow weed, cottonwood, tamarisk, cattail, quailbush, wolfberry, mesquite and various sedges and grasses. The Riverside Bridge bisects the river in Nevada and the river has unique qualities to the north and south of the bridge. To the north, the river is channelized and much of the native riparian habitat is sustained via runoff from irrigation from private landowners. Immediately to the south of the Riverside Bridge there are numerous meanders in the Virgin River with a range of native riparian vegetation types, including some marshes and several patches of native willow. Depending on the water level of Lake Mead, a delta that forms where the river meets the lake.

The water flows of the Virgin River are influenced by mountain snow pack in southwestern Utah, and the river is subject to flooding from summer monsoon events. Diversions on the river include the Quail Reservoir in Utah, and urban uses in Mesquite, Nevada, and St. George, Utah. Land ownership is a patchwork of BLM, private, state lands, Nevada Department of Wildlife, Bureau of Reclamation, and National Park Service.

Land uses include agriculture, tourism and recreation, urban-suburban development, conservation and research, and water management.

Birds

The Virgin River is one of the few rivers in Nevada that still has meanders and is not influenced by dams within its Nevada reach. The Virgin River is also the only intact river in the Mojave Desert of Nevada. All of the Endangered birds in Nevada occur on the Virgin River and many of the birds identified in the Lowland Riparian section of the Nevada Partners in Flight Bird Conservation Plan occur on the Virgin River. Other key species include Bell's Vireo, Blue Grosbeak, Lucy's Warbler, Yellow-breasted Chat, and Peregrine Falcon.

Species used to identify the Virgin River IBA and the criteria met by the site. Criteria codes are discussed in Appendix II.

Species	Year	Season	Min	Max	Units	Confirmed
American White Pelican	2002	non-br	300	500	individuals	NV1, NV3g
Yuma Clapper Rail	2002	breeding	20	30	individuals	NV3g
Yellow-billed Cuckoo	2002	breeding	6	10	individuals	NV1, NV2, NV3g
Southwestern Willow Flycatcher	2002	breeding	0	60	individuals	NV1, NV2, NV3g

Conservation Issues

Invasive plant species, particularly tamarisk, are a threat to the integrity of this system. Significant stretches of the river have been entirely taken over by this species with negative consequences. However, some bird species do use tamarisk for nesting, and it does provide cover for migrating passerines. Agency efforts to control this species are building momentum.

The city of Mesquite lies at the upper end of the Nevada portion of the Virgin River watershed. Mesquite is experiencing rapid growth, and groundwater withdrawals to meet demands for lawns, golf courses, and basic household needs could threaten surface flows in the river. A recent flood event in the Virgin River prompted the city of Mesquite to implement controversial emergency management actions that included bulldozing and straightening a section of the river. While city management was preoccupied with moving water through the Mesquite section of the river as quickly as possible, this sort of geomorphic tinkering creates major structural problems for the river.

The Southern Nevada Water Authority (SNWA), representing the water interests of Las Vegas, also has surface water rights in the Virgin River. SNWA has been evaluating how to transfer this water because the Colorado River Pact does not allow SNWA to simply withdraw their water shares from Lake Mead, into which the Virgin River drains. Ultimately, a pipeline to move water from the Virgin River to Las Vegas could be built, likely requiring a water storage facility on or adjacent to the river. Should they occur, these withdrawals will certainly impact the integrity of the river below the withdrawal point.

Visiting the Site

The best section of this IBA for visiting bird watchers lies between Riverside on NV 170 and Mesquite. Extensive private lands mean roadside viewing, but the community park in Bunkerville is worth a stop in spring or fall.

Walker Lake

Area: 16,801 ha
UTM Easting: 351220
UTM Northing: 4283811

Description

Walker Lake lies at the terminus of the Walker River in western Nevada. The Walker River is one of three major rivers that drain the east side of the Sierra Nevada, and it supports riparian, wetland, riverine, and, at its terminus, a desert lake ecosystem. Walker Lake is a remnant of Pleistocene Lake Lahontan, which covered much of central and northern Nevada during the last ice age.

Walker Lake is bounded to the east and west by arid, jagged, sparsely vegetated, and steep ranges. Mount Grant (IBA), on the west side of the lake, crowns the Wassuk Range at 11,245 feet. The lake itself supports an extremely limited riparian wetland community, mostly restricted in extent to the southern end of the lake. Much of the lake's perimeter is either unvegetated, or supports lowland desert shrub and shrub-steppe communities. A few springs and small tributaries enter the lake from the Wassuk Range.

Immediately north of the lake, the Walker River meanders extensively across the valley floor prior to entering the north end of Walker Lake. This section of the river is essentially a delta, and it supports an expanse of tamarisk, though historically this area was a cottonwood -willow riparian complex. This area, from the border of the Walker River Indian Reservation to the lake, is not included within the boundaries of the IBA. Should restoration efforts in the delta meet with success, expansion of the IBA boundary to include the Walker River delta may be warranted. Land uses at Walker Lake include a managed fishery, conservation and research, and tourism and recreation.

Birds

Walker Lake is recognized as an IBA on the basis of its support of more than 10,000 water birds. Walker Lake provides habitat to Western Snowy Plover,

Common Loon, Western, Clark's, and Eared Grebes, Double-crested Cormorant, White-faced Ibis, Tundra Swan, Snow Goose, Gadwall, Redhead, Ruddy Duck, Northern Shoveler, and American White Pelican. As many as 1,400 Common Loons have been documented on Walker Lake during fall, constituting the largest known inland congregation west of the Mississippi River. Recent radio tracking of a few of these individuals indicates that their breeding grounds are centered in west-central Saskatchewan; their wintering grounds remain unidentified.

Species used to identify Walker Lake IBA and the criteria met by the site. Proposed criteria await the availability of additional data before review by the Nevada IBA TAC. Criteria codes are discussed in Appendix II.

Species	Year	Season	Min	Max	Units	Proposed	Confirmed
Common Loon	1997	migration	--	1,433	adults only		NV2, NV3g, NV3a
Eared Grebe	1999	migration	--	511	individuals		NV3a
Clark's Grebe	1989	migration	--	9,065	individuals	NV3g	NV1, NV3a
White-faced Ibis	1995	migration	---	500	individuals		NV1, NV3e
Ruddy Duck	1998	migration	--	4,375	individuals	NV3g	NV3a
Gadwall	1995	migration	--	3,000	adults only		NV3a
Northern Shoveler	1995	migration	--	2,000	adults only		NV3a
Redhead	1995	migration	--	15,000	unknown	NV3g	NV3a

Snowy Plover (© Bob Goodman)

Conservation Issues

The Walker River is the lifeblood of Walker Lake, but, like many Western rivers, water rights from the river were allocated at a time of atypically high discharge. The Walker River is now over-appropriated; it requires 143 percent of normal flow for water to reach the lake. No consideration has been given to maintaining instream flows to sustain wildlife. Abundant water conditions occur so rarely that the lake essentially receives no water. Since the late 1800s, when excessive water use began, the lake level has dropped more than 136 feet. Because this drop has been driven by evaporation, the water in the lake is so laden with minerals that it cannot support a self-sustaining fishery. The tui chub (a Nevada endemic) can no longer reproduce in the lake. The Lahontan cutthroat trout, once native to these waters and legendary in size and numbers, must be introduced from hatchery stock after a long process of acclimatization. These

113

fish, especially the chub, form the basis of the food chain for Common Loons and other fish-eating birds, and are required for successful migration.

The issue of water diversion is contentious, with upstream agricultural interests pitted against conservation, the Walker River Paiute, and the tenuous economic viability of Hawthorne in particular and Mineral County in general.

Somewhat complicating the issue is the mercury contamination in the lake. The source of the mercury is historic mining activity near the top of the Walker River watershed, principally the towns of Bodie and Aurora. The mercury has washed downstream and now enters the food chain and ultimately concentrates in the top predators (e.g., loons) at the lake. The mercury is so pervasive that cleanup is not realistic. Meanwhile, the presence of the metal is almost certainly detrimental to birds and other wildlife.

Visiting the Site

US 95 skirts the west side of Walker Lake and provides numerous turnouts for viewing the lake and birds resting on its surface. The community of Hawthorne and the Nevada Department of Wildlife have offered a Loon Festival in April of past years with boat tours on the lake to view the migrating birds. The future of this festival is tenuous and intimately tied to the fate of the lake and its loons.

Walker Lake in winter

Washoe Valley

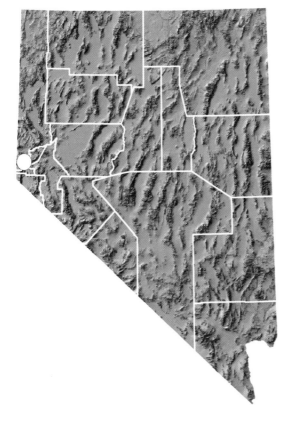

Area: 3,710 ha
UTM Easting: 258209
UTM Northing: 4350508

Description

Washoe Valley IBA is comprised of two shallow ephemeral lakes (Little and Big Washoe Lake), the Scripps WMA, adjacent wet meadows and pastures, and stands of cottonwoods and willows. Lying between the metropolitan centers of Reno and Carson City, and adjacent to the growing community of New Washoe, a surprising amount of open space persists here.

Washoe Valley IBA sits in a narrow and picturesque valley, bounded on the west by the Carson Range (IBA) and on the east by the Virginia Range. Its location in a transition zone between the Sierra Nevada and Great Basin ecoregions adds to its species diversity. The Washoe Valley IBA landscape includes varying amounts of open water (fluctuating with runoff and season), agricultural rangelands, grasslands, shrublands, and emergent marshes.

Although this is a rich system and worthy of conservation efforts, the area has experienced a long litany of changes since Euro-American settlement. The valley has long been an important travel corridor between Reno and Carson City, and historically the V&T Railroad crossed the valley. Today, US 395 crosses through the western side of the IBA and connects Carson City and Reno. This highway experiences a high volume of traffic and fragments the site for terrestrial species. It appears that this fragmentation does not have much impact on the avifauna, but this impact has not been studied. Old Washoe City on the northern boundary of the IBA was the location of one of the first silver mills in Nevada and was briefly an important lumber milling and produce center, providing support primarily for the Comstock mines. Ponderosa pines once bordered the west side of the valley, but Comstock era timbering converted much of the area from forest to grasslands and shrublands.

Land uses today include agricultural activities, residential development, conservation, transportation corridors, and tourism and recreation.

Birds

More than 215 bird species have been recorded in Washoe Valley and more than 100 species nest there in wet years (Eidel 1996). The heron rookery in the Scripps WMA at the north end of the valley contains hundreds of nests of Great Blue Heron, Snowy Egret, Great Egret, Black-crowned Night Heron, and White-faced Ibis. This is the only rookery in the region; the next closest rookery is in the Carson Valley IBA to the south.

The wetlands surrounding Washoe Lake host a breeding population of Virginia and Sora rails, shorebirds, Wilson's Snipe, and waterfowl. Willet, which are not common in the more extensive Lahontan Valley IBA to the east, breed in Washoe Valley. Wilson's Phalarope also breed in the valley. American White Pelicans are common on the lake in breeding and migration, though in breeding season the birds are migrants from distant nesting colonies such as Anaho Island (Pyramid Lake IBA). Loggerhead Shrikes and Sage Thrashers breed in the sagebrush of the Washoe Valley.

Adjacent to Washoe Lake and Little Washoe Lake are extensive wet meadows. This habitat type is suitable for Long-billed Curlew, though only transient birds are known from this site. Other wading birds take advantage of this habitat for foraging. Seasonal ponds fed by snow melt from the nearby Carson Range support waterfowl in spring and winter.

A Nevada Department of Transportation wetland mitigation site at the south end of the IBA is becoming increasingly important for waterbirds, some of which breed at the site. The mitigation area was established to compensate for wetland impacts from the construction of US 395. The site offers opportunities for outreach and education.

Other key breeding species in this landscape include Black-crowned Night Heron, Cinnamon Teal, Gadwall, Northern Pintail, Northern Shoveler, and Ruddy Duck.

Species used to identify Washoe Valley IBA and the criteria met by the site. Criteria codes are discussed in Appendix II.

Species	Year	Season	Min	Max	Units	Confirmed
American Avocet	1997	breeding	5	43	birds/km²*	NV1
Black-necked Stilt	1997	breeding	5	43	birds/km²*	NV1
Clark's Grebe	1997	breeding	1	4	birds/km²*	NV1
Great Egret	1997	breeding	1	4	birds/km²*	NV3e
Snowy Egret	1997	breeding	1	4	birds/km²*	NV3e
White-faced Ibis	1997	breeding	>44	--	birds/km²*	NV1, NV3e

*Density estimated in appropriate habitat in the appropriate season.

Conservation Issues

The two lakes at the core of this IBA are on state lands and are therefore protected and managed against most threats in this area. Invasive weeds are established in isolated areas and it is likely that constant management will be needed to suppress these populations. A large historic ranch at this site was recently acquired by The Conservation Fund in cooperation with the BLM, assuring that this important area will be secure against development. Outside of these publicly owned areas lie private ranches, and these are coming under increasing development pressure. This poses a threat to the integrity of the site and disproportionately affects the wet meadow and pasture/grasslands habitats.

Visiting the Site

Two locations within this IBA are particularly good for bird watchers. The Scripps WMA on the north end of the IBA is worth a stop. Another good location is on the south end of the IBA at the Washoe mitigation ponds, which has two viewing platforms and a network of trails along the dyke system. Both of these places may close during breeding season to protect nesting birds.

Washoe Lake (© Bob Goodman)

Wee Thump Joshua Tree Forest

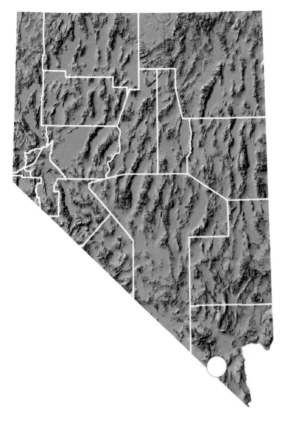

Area: 12,437 ha
UTM Easting: 674723
UTM Northing: 3929124

Description

The phrase wee thump is of Paiute origin and means ancient ones, and, in this case, references the spectacular Joshua tree forest covering this site. The eastern boundary of the IBA lies about six miles west of Searchlight and stretches to the eastern slope of the McCullough Mountains. The IBA takes in the densest stands of the Joshua forest. NV 164 crosses the IBA on the east-west axis, and a few two-track dirt roads also penetrate the area. In 2002 about a third of the site was designated wilderness.

The site's outstanding feature is reflected in its name, an extensive, relatively dense, and vigorous Joshua tree forest. Any approach to the area crosses through miles of low desert shrub habitat, with only the occasional Joshua tree and the jagged cliffs of the surrounding mountain ranges to punctuate the desert. The Joshua tree forest stands out for the fact that it offers considerably more habitat diversity than the surrounding landscape, including cavities for such species as Ladder-backed Woodpecker, Northern Flicker, and the only known breeding population of Gilded Flicker in Nevada. Although the area has been grazed in the past, the understory is now lush by Mojave Desert standards and supports a diversity of grasses, shrubs, and cacti. Although the botanic affinity of the site is clearly Mojave Desert, the underlying topography is basin and range. The forest stretches from the valley floor west of Searchlight, and up and over the lower elevations of the McCullough Range.

Land uses at this site include conservation and research, wilderness, tourism and recreation, hunting, and a transportation corridor.

Birds

Nest cavities are one resource that is almost exclusively absent from desert sites, and it is this resource that makes Wee Thump unique. The ancient Joshua trees, many estimated to be over 250 years old, offer cavities and so there is a unique guild of cavity nesters at the site. In fact, the cavities not only provide important nesting opportunities but also offer winter refuges for certain bird species as well. These birds include Western Bluebird, Gilded Flicker, Northern Flicker, and Hairy Woodpeckers. Ash-throated Flycatchers are abundant here. Birds from the nearby McCullough Mountains (e.g., Northern Flicker) may migrate altitudinally to Wee Thump in winter to weather the colder season.

Species used to identify Wee Thump Joshua Tree IBA and the criteria met by the site. Proposed criteria await the availability of additional data prior to evaluation by the Nevada IBA TAC. Criteria codes are discussed in Appendix II.

Species	Year	Season	Min	Max	Units	Proposed	Confirmed
Gilded Flicker	2000	breeding	20	--	pairs	NV3g	NV2
Gray Flycatcher	2000	breeding	--	--	--		NV1, NV2
Scott's Oriole	2000	breeding	0	43	pairs/km^2*		NV2
Loggerhead Shrike	2000	breeding	0	4	pairs/km^2*		NV1, NV2
Ash-throated Flycatcher	2003	breeding	1	43	pairs/km^2*		NV1, NV2
Phainopepla	2000	breeding	1	43	pairs/km^2*		NV1, NV2
Bendire's Thrasher	2000	breeding	20	--	pairs		NV1, NV2
Gray Vireo	2000	breeding	60	--	pairs		NV1, NV2

*Density estimated in appropriate habitat in the appropriate season.

Conservation Issues

A few two-track travel corridors do penetrate this area. For the most part it appears that recreationists have obeyed regulations and stayed on the sanctioned road system. Some vandalism of the Joshua trees has occurred (shooting, cutting), and there is some littering, though both of these problems appear to be minor at this time.

Visiting the Site

NV 164 makes the short traverse west of Searchlight to the California border

and crosses through the middle of this IBA. There are several pullouts and, as mentioned above, a few two-track gravel roads accessible from NV 164. Any of these spots are worth a stop and a short walk into the Joshua tree forest.

The distinctive landscape of the Wee Thump Joshua Tree IBA

Wellington-Pine Grove Hills

Area: 102,797 ha
UTM Easting: 308823
UTM Northing: 4273978

Description

Located along the California border, this site is roughly contiguous with the Bodie Hills IBA recognized by the California IBA Program (Cooper 2004). The site includes the population center in Nevada for the bi-state population of the Greater Sage-Grouse. Preliminary genetic analysis of the bi-state birds indicates that they are distinct from surrounding populations (Oyler-McCance et al. 2005). Additional genetic sampling and studies on Greater Sage-Grouse physical and behavioral traits need to be completed before an appropriate conclusion can be made about whether the bi-state birds warrant designation as a sub-species or species.

Because of the 5,000 foot-plus elevation range, the habitat varies from desert shrub along the lower boundaries to conifer at the highest elevations. Piñon-juniper forest is extensive, but the habitat is spatially complex because it is broken by mountain meadows and parklands and stringers of aspens and cottonwoods along riparian zones like Desert Creek. Wellington Hills and the Sweetwater Range form prominent mountains in this IBA.

Land uses in this IBA include rangelands, hunting and fishing, tourism and recreation, water supply management, and conservation.

Birds

High quality sagebrush habitat supports a sagebrush-obligate community, the highlight of which is the bi-state Greater Sage-Grouse. Riparian stringers of aspen and cottonwood are multi-aged stands with numerous cavities and a well developed understory.

Species used to identify the Wellington-Pine Grove Hills IBA and the criteria met by the site. Proposed criteria await evaluation by the National Technical Committee. Criteria codes are discussed in Appendices II and III.

Species	Year	Season	Min	Max	Units	Proposed	Confirmed
Greater Sage-Grouse	2002	breeding	--	375	pairs	A1	NV1
Sage Thrasher	1999	breeding	1	4	pairs/km²*		NV1
Western Bluebird	1999	breeding	1	4	pairs/km²*		NV1
Vesper Sparrow	1999	breeding	1	4	pairs/km²*		NV1
MacGillivray's Warbler	1999	breeding	5	43	pairs/km²*		NV1
Pinyon Jay	1999	breeding	5	43	pairs/km²*		NV1
Sage Sparrow	1999	breeding	0	4	pairs/km²*		NV1
Yellow-breasted Chat	1997	breeding	1	4	pairs/km²*		NV1
Cooper's Hawk	1999	breeding	0	4	pairs/km²*		NV1
Juniper Titmouse	1999	breeding	5	43	pairs/km²*		NV1
Red-naped Sapsucker	2002	breeding	1	4	pairs/km²*		NV1

*Density estimated in appropriate habitat and in the appropriate season.

Conservation Issues

The piñon-juniper forest on this site appears to be expanding at the expense of the sagebrush habitat type. While perhaps beneficial to piñon-juniper species, this trend is certainly detrimental to sagebrush obligates. The absence of fire as a mechanism to reset the successional clock may in part be to blame. However, with fire comes cheatgrass and an altered fire cycle that precludes the development of sagebrush communities. The answer may lie in using other management techniques to create openings in the piñon-juniper and encourage habitat heterogeneity. Working against a mechanical or otherwise anthropogenic approach is the fact that much of this landscape is remote and inaccessible.

The portions of the Wellington Hills and Pine Grove Hills that are accessible constitute a popular recreation destination. The land management agency (Forest Service) needs to carefully monitor and regulate visitation, particularly in the form of ORV use, in order to protect habitat integrity.

One of the key lek sites for the Greater Sage-Grouse lies on private land that has been platted for residential development. Housing development would destroy the lek and may contribute to a decline of the bi-state population of the Greater Sage-Grouse.

Desert Creek Peak, Wellington Hills

Visiting the Site

FR 027 follows Desert Creek and includes access to Desert Creek Campground. The Rosachi Ranch (Forest Service), near the intersection of NV 338 and FR 028, is under restoration and is worth a visit.

References

Able, K. P. 2003. Wolves to Warblers: The Tentacles of Top Carnivores. Birding 35:384-392.

American Bird Conservancy. 2004. Globally Important Bird Areas of the United States. Map.

Ammon, E. M. 2002. Changes in the bird community of the lower Truckee River, Nevada, 1868-2001. Great Basin Birds 5:13-20.

Arsenault, D. P., G. E. Wilson, and L. A. Neel. 2003. Flammulated Owls in the Spring Mountains, Nevada. Avian Research Center of Nevada, Reno, NV.

Beason, J., and S. A. Jentsch, 2001. Breeding Birds of the McCullough Mountains. Great Basin Birds 4:25-26.

BirdLife International. 2004a. Important Bird Areas. http://www.birdlife.net/action/science/sites/index.html. Accessed June 7.

BirdLife International. 2004b. Threatened Birds of the World 2004. Lynx Edicions and BirdLife International, Barcelona and Cambridge, UK.

Biological Resources Research Center. 2004. Spring Mountains. http://www.brrc.unr.edu/mtn/html/springr.html. Accessed March 31.

BIO/WEST, Inc. 2001. An Ecological Evaluation of the Lower Virgin River Riparian Corridor. Final Report.

Boone, J. 2004. Key Pittman Wildlife Management Area. http://members.cox.net/jlboone3/Outside_LV/Outside_NE/Pahranagat/Key_Pittman/Key_Pittman.htm. Accessed March 29.

Boyles, M. 1998-2002. National Park Service Databases: Bald Eagle Surveys, Peregrine Falcon Surveys, MAPS Banding Records. Unpublished.

Chipley, R. M., G. H. Fenwick, M. J. Parr, and D. N. Pashley 2003. The American Bird Conservancy Guide to the 500 Most Important Bird Areas in the United States. Random House, New York.

Chisholm, G., and L. A. Neel 2002. Birds of the Lahontan Valley: A Guide to Nevada's Wetland Oasis. University of Nevada Press, Reno.

Clark, J. L. 1993. Nevada Wildlife Viewing Guide. Falcon Press, Helena, MT.

Cooper, D. S. 2004. Important Bird Areas of California. Audubon California, Pasadena.

Crossley, G. J. 1999. A Guide to Critical Bird Habitat in Pennsylvania. Pennsylvania Audubon Society, Harrisburg.

Cullinan, T. 2001. Important Bird Areas of Washington. Audubon Washington, Olympia.

Dahl, T. E., and C. F. Johnson. 1991. Status and trends of wetlands in the conterminous United States: mid-1970's to mid-1980's. U.S. Fish and Wildlife Service, Washington, DC.

Dobkin, D. S. 1998. Conservation and Management of Neotropical Migrant Land Birds in the Great Basin. University of Idaho Press, Moscow.

Duncan, C. D., B. Abel, D. Ewert, M. L. Ford, S. Mabey, D. Mehlman, P. Patterson, R. Sutter, and M. Woodrey. 2002. Protecting stopover sites for forest-dwelling migratory landbirds: A Nature Conservancy issue paper. The Nature Conservancy, Migratory Bird Program, Portland, ME.

Earnst, S. L., J. Ballard, and D. Dobkin. 2002. Riparian songbird monitoring on Hart Mountain and Sheldon National Wildlife Refuges - 2000-2001 and a comparison to 1991-1993. USGS Forest and Rangeland Ecosystem Science Center, Boise, ID.

Eidel, J. J. 1996. The breeding and migratory birds of ephemeral Lake Washoe. Report to the Nevada Division of Wildlife and Nevada Division of Parks.

Great Basin Bird Observatory. 2002. Unpublished Breeding Bird Atlas Data. Great Basin Bird Observatory, Reno, NV.

Great Basin Bird Observatory. 2004. Aquatic Bird Count database query for Lake Mead. http://www.gbbo.org/abc_query.php3. December 30.

Grimmett, R. 1989. Important Bird Areas of Europe. International Council of Bird Preservation.

Hanford, F. S. 1903. The summer birds of Washoe Lake, Nevada. Condor 5:50-52.

Holman, G. 2000. Bird Habitat Study at Swan Lake. University of Nevada, Reno. April.

Hughes, J. M. 1999. Yellow-billed cuckoo (*Coccyzus americanus*). Pages 1-28 in A. Poole, and F. B. Gill, editors. The Birds of North America. The Birds of North America, Inc., Philadelphia, PA.

Kushlan, J. A., M. J. Steinkamp, K. C. Parsons, J. Capp, M. A. Cruz, M. Coulter, I. Davidson, L. Dickson, N. Edelson, R. Elliot, R. M. Erwin, S. Hatch, S. Kress, R. Milko, S. Miller, K. Mills, R. Paul, T. Phillips, J. E. Saliva, B. Sydeman, J. Trapp, J. Wheeler, and K. Wohl. 2002. Waterbird Conservation for the Americas: The North American Waterbird Conservation Plan, Version 1. Waterbird Conservation for the Americas, Washington, DC.

Lahontan Audubon Society. 2000. A Birding Guide to Reno and Beyond. Lahontan Audubon Society, Reno, Nevada.

Lahontan Audubon Society. 2004. Nevada Birding Map. Lahontan Audubon Society, Reno.

Lund, B. 2002. Lower Muddy Valley Wash Bird Survey Project. The Nature Conservancy Southern Nevada Field Office. Unpublished.

Mac, M. J., P. A. Opler, C. E. Puckett Haecker, and P. D. Doran. 1988. Great Basin-Mojave Desert Region. Status and Trends of the Nation's Biological

Resources. U.S. Department of the Interior, U.S. Geological Survey, Reston, Virginia.

Manomet Center for Conservation Science. 2004. Western Hemisphere Shorebird Reserve Network. http://www.manomet.org/WHSRN/viewsite.php?id=42. Accessed February 9.

McKernan, R. L., and G. Braden. 2002. Status, distribution, and habitat affinities of the Southwestern Willow Flycatcher along the Lower Colorado River Year 6-2001. Report to the U.S. Bureau of Reclamation.

McLane, A. R. 1978. Silent Cordilleras. Camp Nevada, Reno, NV.

McLane, A. 1995. A Cultural Resources Inventory of NANGST in Lemmon Valley, Nevada. Desert Research Institute. April.

Medin, D. E., B. L. Welch, and W. P. Clary. 2000. Bird habitat relationships along a Great Basin elevational gradient. Research paper RMRS-RP-23. Fort Collins, CO: U.S. Department of Agriculture, Forest Service, Rocky Mountain Research Station.

Moore, F. R. 2000. Preface. Studies in Avian Biology 20:1-3.

Moore, R. 1997. Bird Survey of NANGST Wetlands. University of Nevada, Reno. October.

Morrison, R. I. G., J. Gill, R. E., B. A. Harrington, S. Skagen, G. W. Page, C. L. Gratto-Trevor, and H. S. M. 2001. Estimates of shorebird populations in North America. Canadian Wildlife Service, Ottawa, Ontario.

NABCI (North American Bird Conservation Initiative). 2005. Integrated Bird Conservation in the United States. http://www.nabci-us.org/nabci.html. Accessed February 11.

National Audubon Society. 2004a. Success Stories. http://www.audubon.org/bird/iba/success_stories.html. Accessed June 10.

National Audubon Society. 2004b. How will IBAs help Birds? http://www.audubon.org/bird/iba/help_birds.html. Accessed June 16.

Nevada Department of Wildlife. 2004. Greater Sage-Grouse Conservation Plan for Nevada and Eastern California. Nevada Department of Wildlife. First Edition. June 30.

Neel, L. A., editor. 1999. Nevada Partners in Flight Bird Conservation Plan. Partners in Flight, Nevada Working Group. Reno.

Nevada Army National Guard. 2001. Integrated Natural Resources Management Plan. September.

Nevada Division of Wildlife. 1996-2001. Job Progress Reports. Endangered Species and Passerine Bird Sections.

Nevada Wilderness. 2002. High Rock Canyon Wilderness. www.nevadawilderness.org/northwest/highrockcyn.htm. Accessed June 24.

Nevada Wildlife Federation. 2004. Sheldon National Wildlife Refuge. http://www.nvwf.org/nevada/places/pl_sheld.htm. Accessed April 9.

O'Farrell, M. J. 1995. Progress Report—Autumn Bat Survey on the Lower Virgin River Riparian Corridor. Prepared for BIO/WEST, Inc. Logan, UT.

O'Farrell, M. J. 1996. Spring Bat Survey on the Lower Virgin River Riparian Corridor. Prepared for BIO/WEST, Inc. Logan, UT.

Oyler-McCance, S. J., S. E. Taylor, and T. W. Quinn. 2005. A multilocus population genetic survey of the greater sage-grouse across their range. Molecular Ecology 14:1293-1310.

Pearson, T. G. 1937. Adventures in Bird Protection. D. Appleton-Century Co., New York.

Plissner, J. H., S. M. Haig, and L. W. Oring. 2000. Post breeding movements of American Avocets and implications for wetland connectivity in the western Great Basin. The Auk 117:290-298.

Ramsar. 2005. A Directory of Wetlands of International Importance. http://www.wetlands.org/RDB/Directory.html. Accessed September 30.

Rich, T. D., C. J. Beardmore, H. Berlanga, P. J. Blancher, M. S. W. Bradstreet, G. S. Butcher, D. Demarest, E. H. Dunn, W. C. Hunter, E. Inigo-Elias, J. A. Kennedy, A. Martell, A. Panjabi, D. N. Pashley, K. V. Rosenberg, C. Rustay, S. Wendt, and T. Will. 2004. Partners in Flight North American Landbird Conservation Plan. Cornell Lab of Ornithology, Ithaca, NY.

Ridgway, R. 1877. Part III, Ornithology, in C. King, Report of the Geological Exploration of the Fortieth Parallel. U.S. Army Engineer Department, Professional Paper 18.

Sauer, J. R., J. E. Hines, and J. Fallon. 2004. The North American Breeding Bird Survey, Results and Analysis 1966 - 2003. Version 2004.1. USGS Patuxent Wildlife Research Center, Laurel, MD. http://www.mbr-pwrc.usgs.gov/bbs/bbs.html.

Sedgewick, J. A. 2000. Willow flycatcher (*Empidonax traillii*) in A. Poole, and F. B. Gill, editors. The Birds of North America. The Birds of North America, Inc., Philadelphia, PA.

Sillet, T. S., and R. T. Holmes. 2002. Variation in survivorship of a migratory songbird throughout its annual cycle. Journal of Animal Ecology 71:296-308.

Smith, J. P. 2005. Fall 2004 Flammulated Owl Migration Study in the Goshute Mountains of Northeastern Nevada. Hawkwatch International, Inc. Salt Lake City, UT.

Smith, J. P. and M. S. Vekasy. 2001. Fall 2000 Raptor Migration Studies in the Goshute Mountains of Northeastern Nevada. Hawkwatch International, Inc. Salt Lake City, UT.

Soussan, T. 2003. Vegas owns up to water woes. Albuquerque Journal, Albuquerque, June 15.

Swan Lake Advisory Board. 2000. Master Plan, Swan Lake Nature Study Area, July 1997, Updated February 2000. Reno, NV.

The Nature Conservancy 2001. Great Basin: An Ecoregion-based Conservation Blueprint. The Nature Conservancy of Nevada, Reno, NV.

Tracy, R., and R. Espinoza. 1998. An Inventory of Herpetofauna. University of Nevada, Reno.

University of Nevada, Reno. 1995. Botanical and Animal/Bird Survey of the Stead Training Complex. September.

U.S. Environmental Protection Agency. 2005. Carson River Mercury Site. http://yosemite.epa.gov/r9/sfund/overview.nsf/507c94f730e0ebf4882569

58005cda5f/82004c6c4169ae528825660b007ee640?OpenDocument.
Accessed September 20.

U.S. Fish and Wildlife Service. 2001. Ruby Lake NWR Annual Narrative Report,
Calendar Year 2000.

U.S. Fish and Wildlife Service. 2004a. Ash Meadows National Wildlife Refuge.
U.S. Fish and Wildlife Service, Amargosa Valley, NV.

U.S. Fish and Wildlife Service. 2004b. Ash Meadows National Wildlife Refuge.
http://desertcomplex.fws.gov/ashmeadows/index.htm. Accessed February
11.

U.S. Fish and Wildlife Service. 2004c. Pahranagat National Wildlife Refuge.
http://desertcomplex.fws.gov/pahranagat/. Accessed March 29.

U.S. Fish and Wildlife Service. 2004d. Anaho Island National Wildlife Refuge.
http://stillwater.fws.gov/anaho.html. Accessed March 30.

U.S. Fish and Wildlife Service. 2004e. Desert National Wildlife Range. U.S. Fish
and Wildlife Service. http://desertcomplex.fws.gov/desertrange/index.htm.
Accessed September 22.

U.S. General Accounting Office. 1993. Livestock grazing on western riparian
areas. Page 44. U.S. General Accounting Office, Gaithersburg, MD.

U.S. Geological Survey. 1998. Distribution and Status of Avifauna Utilizing
Riparian Habitats within Clark County, Nevada. Report to U.S. Bureau of
Reclamation.

Walters, J. 1997-2002. Collected observations from field trips to Meadow Valley
Wash. Unpublished.

Webb, R. H., G. J. McCabe, R. Hereford, and C. Wilkowske. 2004. Climatic
Fluctuations, Drought, and Flow of the Colorado River. U.S. Geological
Survey.

Wells, J. V. 1998. Important Bird Areas in New York State. National Audubon
Society, Albany, NY.

Wetlands International. 2002. Waterbird population estimates – Third edition.
Wetlands International, Wageningen, The Netherlands.

Wiesenborn, W. D. 1996. Salt cedar impacts on salinity, water, fire frequency,
and flooding. Salt Cedar Management Workshop.

Wuerthner, G. 1992. Nevada Mountain Ranges. American & World Geographic
Publishing, Helena, MT.

Yates, M. 1999. Walker Lake Satellite Telemetry Common Loon Study. Great
Basin Birds 2:68-69.

Yates, M. 1999. Tracking Walker Lake's Loons. The Loon Call, page 7.

Yates, M. 2000. Nevada: Walker Lake Loon Research. The Loon Call, pages 4-5.

Yates, M. A., M. R. Fuller, D. Evers, J. Paruk, and K. Kenow. 2003. Migrant
common loons at Walker Lake, Nevada: characterization of range, source(s)
and effects of mercury contamination, and loss of fishery. Boise State
University, Boise, ID.

Appendices

Appendix I – Other Sites Evaluated as IBAs

When the Nevada IBA Program started in late 2001, the first step taken was to compile a list of all sites in Nevada that should be evaluated as potential IBAs. The list was generated by interviewing birders, wildlife biologists, land managers, and staff at other conservation organizations and by reviewing published literature. This list was compiled with the recognition that evaluation of the sites would take many forms, from site visits, further discussion with knowledgeable individuals, review of published and gray literature, to preparation of full IBA nominations and evaluation by the Nevada TAC. A site could be dropped from further consideration at any one of these steps if it became apparent that the site would not meet any of the IBA criteria. Sites were also dropped from the nomination process if data could not be generated to fill a nomination.

Although the sites below are not currently Nevada IBAs, it is worth publishing this list of sites for a number of reasons. First, many of these sites remain intriguing landscapes and certainly have the potential to become IBAs. But for almost all of them we lack sufficient understanding of the extent, composition, and seasonal patterns of use of the landscapes by the bird communities. In a nutshell, we need more data in order to give these places proper consideration. This need not be data collected by rigorously trained technicians with college degrees. We need citizen-scientists with an ability to identify birds and keep a count to go bird watching in these areas. The data needs are simple: how many birds, where, and when. What is difficult is the logistics–getting people out to these places, most of which are remote from population centers.

If you are a bird watcher and find yourself in one of these areas, we hope you will take the time to report your findings. In the long run this information informs many projects across the state, not just the IBA Program. There are a number of efforts to track bird trends across Nevada and across the nation. Placing bird lists in public forums where they can form a permanent record does a great service to the birding and conservation communities. There are many ways to accomplish this task, including the Nevada Birds List Server (list.audubon.org/archives/nvbirds.html), eBird (www.ebird.org), or by getting involved in organized survey activities like the Nevada All-bird Monitoring Program (www.gbbo.org) and the North American Breeding Bird Survey (www.pwrc.usgs.gov/bbs/). The IBA Program would welcome additional information about birds at any of these sites, regardless of whether or not they have already passed through the nomination process.

The following sites had enough data to be evaluated on some level–either in a full IBA nomination or in a review of existing conditions prior to making a decision to filing a complete nomination. A brief discussion of their bird values and their known status is provided.

Porter Springs

This desert oasis about 30 miles northeast of Lovelock was nominated for the diversity of migrant songbirds that have been recorded there. The site came up for review by the Nevada IBA TAC and presented some significant challenges for the group. The site is representative of the many small isolated desert wetlands that offer migrating songbirds a respite on their long journey.

Defining a significant stopover site for songbirds is difficult, and in the end something that the Nevada IBA TAC could not do. At the root of the problem is a lack of data and therefore a lack of understanding about how songbirds use the landscape during migration. The problem is not unique to Nevada, though Gulf States and some East Coast states have invested time, money, and effort into investigating this phenomenon.

The late Jack Walters visited Porter Springs for over 10 years, compiling a remarkable data set for the site. Jack's efforts documented over 160 species at this little oasis. No single migratory species appears there in great numbers, at least not on a single day. And they probably do not stay long, perhaps a day before moving on to the next stepping stone. In the evolving language of migration stopovers Porter Springs is a *convenience store*, a "forested patch in a non-forested matrix, located along migratory routes...[providing] habitat where birds can safely rest and at least minimally refuel as they move through to higher quality sites..." (Duncan et al. 2002).

What the Nevada IBA TAC has been unable to resolve is where Porter Springs sits in the spectrum of stopovers in Nevada, because our objective is to recognize the best 10 percent or so of these sites as IBAs. Some TAC members were concerned that, if Porter Springs became an IBA, every mud puddle surrounded by tamarisk would also be nominated. There is a fine line separating important *birding* areas from Important Bird Areas. Certainly Porter Springs does not offer the kind of stopover habitat provided by Oasis Valley IBA or Ash Meadows IBA. But if Porter Springs gets a few thousand of our birds another 30 miles along their flyway to the next convenience store, then perhaps it is indeed an Important Bird Area. Irrespective of our confusion and indecision, the birds come and go every spring and fall at Porter Springs, and it is worth a trip up there to see the phenomenon.

South Fork State Recreation Area

This site southwest of Elko does support a large number of birds, particularly during migration and winter months. However, the birds which occur here in greatest numbers are not of conservation concern, and the few individuals that show up that do represent species of conservation concern do not occur here in significant enough numbers to warrant special management at this site. An additional factor in the decision not to recognize this site as an IBA was that it was established for water storage and as a recreation site. As a consequence, the site is managed for goals other than enhancing and preserving habitat. Little emergent marsh vegetation exists around the reservoir, and there is a limited expanse of mud flat at the south end of the reservoir for shorebirds.

In spite of these limitations, two things are noteworthy. First, this is a great place to go bird watching if you're in the Elko area (see Lahontan Audubon Society 2004). Second, the reservoir is relatively new, habitat at the site could improve naturally over time, and bird use of the site could increase to the point that it would be worth reevaluation as an IBA.

Lovelock Valley

Lovelock Valley was suggested as a site because of the raptors that congregate there in winter months, roosting in cottonwood trees and spending their days foraging in the winter-fallowed hay fields. On good days peak numbers of raptors appear to meet or slightly exceed "Criterion NV 3(d) Congregations of raptors: ...The site is...a winter concentration area used by at least 100 raptors." However, the cottonwood trees, all on private lands, are senescent and full access to the groves by cattle precludes regeneration. As a consequence, without intervention the cottonwoods will die of old age in the not-too-distant future with no new trees established to replace them.

Desatoya Mountains

The report of this range as supporting a high concentration of Northern Goshawks could not be substantiated. With only a few isolated perennial water courses and their attendant aspen groves, it appears that suitable habitat for this species in this range is limited.

North Fork Humboldt River

It is true that all perennial water in Nevada is important to birds and other wildlife to some degree. However, like the vast majority of streams and rivers in the state, the North Fork of the Humboldt River has been significantly degraded by more than a century of human manipulation. The river is one of the better ones in the region, and significant effort is likely to be focused on restoration and enhancement in the future. The nearby Mary's River has demonstrated that a shift in management can result in rapid recovery of a stream system. With management changes on the North Fork, it is a site that the IBA Program should reevaluate in 5-10 years.

Massacre Lake, Duck Lake, Calcutta-Cow-Alkali Lakes Complex

The northwest corner of the state is remote, beautiful, and fascinating. Among its points of interest is a network of playa lakes. In years of higher precipitation these playa lakes catch runoff and contain anywhere from a sheen to a few feet of water. Some of the lakes then bloom with brine shrimp released from their long anhydrobiotic state by the presence of water. These brine shrimp in turn support an array of shore birds that are tolerant of saline conditions–American Avocet, Black-necked Stilt, Wilson's Phalarope, and possibly Snowy Plover. More data on bird use of these playas is needed to evaluate their potential as an IBA complex. Plissner et al. (2000) documented movements of American Avocets over distances up to 200 km in the Oregon, California, Nevada region, in part to exploit food outbreaks at playa lakes. It is likely that this particular complex of lakes is a part of this movement pattern and should form part of a landscape level approach to managing habitat for American Avocets and other shorebirds.

Hays Canyon Range

This range on the Nevada-California border has a number of aspen groves and stands of mountain mahogany, both of which are of conservation interest. Upon closer inspection, these forest stands were found to have been badly degraded by cattle that have sought shade under the canopies and devastated the forest understory. This understory component is critical to forest regeneration and to support the full suite of species typical of healthy examples of aspen and mountain mahogany.

Virginia Range

Habitat in this range has been degraded by a variety of historic and current practices, and riparian habitat in particular has been hard hit by unregulated ORV use. There is much ongoing interest in the range, principally by TNC and the BLM, the principal land management agency for the site. The range may constitute a unique site where otherwise isolated populations of Sierra birds and Great Basin birds (e.g., Orange-crowned Warbler) overlap their ranges (T. Floyd, 2002, pers. comm). If management changes result in improved habitat conditions, the Virginia Range may warrant reconsideration.

Pine Nut Mountains

The Pine Nut Mountains, just east of Carson City and Carson Valley, have also been significantly altered by humans. The range was probably clearcut by charcoal makers during the Comstock mining era in the mid-to-late 1800s. The range is now forested again, but ORV use is high. A small but important population of Greater Sage-Grouse lingers in the range and is the focus of management interest. Pinyon Jay populations may also be significant. For a variety of reasons, including burgeoning human populations in nearby Carson City, Dayton, and Carson Valley, the Carson District of the BLM is in the process of re-evaluating and updating its management of this landscape.

Soldier Meadows

This site was identified as a potential hot spot for Long-billed Curlew, a species of national conservation concern. The birds are there but significant numbers have not been documented. Heavy grazing pressure has probably reduced the value of the habitat for Long-billed Curlew. The Winnemucca District of the BLM has published a draft Environmental Impact Statement in part geared to protecting and upgrading facilities at Soldier Meadows.

Fort Mojave

The California portion of Fort Mojave has been identified as a California IBA (Cooper 2004). The Nevada portion was nominated but not recognized because of the extent of land alterations on the Nevada side. Situated on the historic floodplain of the Colorado River, this site probably supported important habitat for a suite of species, especially those relying on mesquite and catclaw acacia for nesting or cover. The current focus of agricultural and economic development by the Pipa Aha Macav–the Fort Mojave Indian Tribe–is concentrated in this area.

South McCullough Mountains

Nominated for potential incorporation into the Wee Thump Joshua Tree IBA, or as a stand-alone IBA. The TAC determined that, while ornithologically interesting, the range does not offer unique habitat or a significant number of any species of conservation concern.

Smoke Creek

This stream begins in wet meadows just upstream from Smoke Creek Reservoir and flows a short distance before disappearing at the edge of the Smoke Creek Desert. The creek has a narrow riparian forest of cottonwoods and willows. Near the terminus of the creek and along the rim of the Smoke Creek Desert are a series of oases that are strikingly similar in appearance to Porter Springs. This whole network probably offers stopover sites for songbirds in migration. The significant portion of this area is in private ownership, and stopover use, including species composition and numbers, remains undocumented.

Mahogany Creek Watershed

This remote watershed near the southeast corner of Sheldon NWR has been set aside for the management of Lahontan cutthroat trout. Grazing is managed intensively to protect water quality in the perennial creek. The aspen and mountain mahogany stands, sagebrush-steppe, and riparian area are in good condition. Documentation of the bird community is lacking. The site was nominated as a Nevada IBA but tabled pending the availability of data.

Mojave Island

This site lies entirely within the Nellis Air Force Bombing and Gunnery Range and is managed under the auspices of the Department of Defense. The site was discovered and documented in the late 1990s as a result of the Nevada Breeding Bird Atlas effort. The site is unusual in that its vegetation and bird communities represent a slice of the transition zone between the Great Basin and Mojave Deserts. This isolated patch of salt desert habitat also sustains a Joshua tree overstory. The avian community is likewise quite diverse. Several of the species observed breeding at this site would not be able to breed in the shadscale habitat without the Joshua tree component.

This site was nominated, reviewed, and accepted with conditions by the Nevada IBA TAC. Although land ownership and land owner notification were not requirements of IBA recognition, an exception to that rule was put forward for this site. This proposed IBA is completely inaccessible to the public. The TAC felt that, without acknowledgment and cooperation from the Department of Defense to assist with long-term monitoring, there would be no tangible benefit to recognizing the site. Several attempts to contact and involve the Nellis Air Force Base were made over the course of more than two years, ultimately without success. Therefore, the site could not receive recognition prior to the publication of this book.

Las Vegas Wash/Henderson Bird Viewing Preserve

When this nomination came before the TAC, it presented a number of challenges. Perhaps of greatest concern was the plume of perchlorate moving under ground and into the wash. This industrial contaminant was a lingering reminder of a munitions plant which had once occupied adjacent property before a lethal accident and explosion brought the operation to an end. The perchlorate contamination had many ramifications for the Lower Colorado River, but of immediate concern to the TAC was the potential impact of this contaminant on birds attracted to the wash. Were we inviting birds to the wash only to contaminate them, possibly impact their reproductive success, or even kill them outright? Research into the effects of percholorate on birds is just beginning, and answers to this question are forthcoming.

The second concern is the basic nature of the Las Vegas Wash system. Although the channel once naturally carried water, most likely during flash floods, it is now carrying continuous flows fed by effluent from Las Vegas waste water treatment. These flows are expected to increase in volume. The problem this creates is not the waste water itself, but the volume of water. The substrate underlying the wash is easily eroded and stream incision and rapid down-cutting is a problem, with the potential of actually degrading rather than improving surrounding habitat.

On top of this, there is a chronic weed and invasive plant problem in the wash. Two of the dominant plants, phragmites (an exotic grass) and tamarisk grow rapidly with an abundance of water, generating a tremendous amount of biomass. Then the plants dry out. The wash has also become a magnet for the homeless, who intentionally or not appear to be responsible for setting fire to the abundant biomass on a frequent basis–at least once or twice each year.

Finally, as far as species of concern go, the numbers in Las Vegas Wash are not impressive. The species of concern that have been documented there appear to be passing through in migration. This is an important role for a site to play, but even so only the occasional Willow Flycatcher (for example) seems to touch down here before moving on to better habitat.

These obstacles are being addressed. There is a tremendous amount of energy and money going into the wash to stabilize the system, control weeds, and make the area an inviting green space that will warrant a lot of community pride. If these problems can be resolved, then Las Vegas Wash will certainly warrant re-evaluation as an IBA.

Railroad Valley

Railroad Valley Wildlife Management Area lies just east of the Grant Range and south of US 6 in eastern Nye County. The site is federally and state owned and managed cooperatively by the BLM and the Nevada Department of Wildlife. The site is comprised of a series of impoundments that sustain varying amounts of habitat (depending on water availability) for waterfowl and shorebirds. Physical improvements at the site in 1993 resulted in more consistent water retention and habitat quality. The site has been reasonably well monitored, more consistently so in the recent past thanks to a newly created non-game biologist position covering this region.

Based on available data, waterfowl production rates at the site are probably low but consistent, although predation pressure from coyotes may be a problem. Bird numbers during migration are more impressive, with a one-time count of American Avocets at about 900 individuals. In spite of that one-time peak, overall numbers at the site are too low to meet any IBA criterion.

Lower Truckee River

The Lower Truckee River between Sparks and Pyramid Lake has been the focus of ornithological interest since Ridgway (1877) recorded 107 species of birds on the river in June 1868. The river and its flood plain have also been significantly altered by human activities since Ridgway's investigations (see Ammon 2002). While significant energy is being expended to correct past mismanagement and restore habitats, the project to restore the Truckee River is in its early stages. Nonetheless, the site is recognized as being worthy of evaluation as an IBA. In spite of this, no nomination could be developed for the site.

The sites in the table below were brought to the attention of the IBA Program during the nomination process. No additional information could be generated, so data are also welcomed for these sites. The "potential species of interest" is not an exhaustive list, and anyone interested in these landscapes should consider the entire list of species presented in Appendix II.

Site Name	Potential Species of Interest
Quinn River	Sandhill Crane, Long-billed Curlew, White-faced Ibis, American Avocet
Mason Valley WMA	Swainson's Hawk, Blue Grosbeak, Yellow-breasted Chat, American White Pelican, White-faced Ibis, American Avocet
Humboldt River (various segments)	colonial nesting waterbirds
South Fork Owyhee River	high density cliff-nesting raptors
Pine Forest Range	Greater Sage-Grouse, burrowing owl, snowy plover
Granite Range	rosy finch communal winter roosts; abandoned mines
Independence Mountains	Northern Goshawk, Greater Sage-Grouse
Schell Creek Range	Northern Goshawk, Peregrine Falcon, Flammulated Owl
Artesia Lake	Snowy Plover, American White Pelican, White-faced Ibis, American Avocet
Topaz Lake-Antelope Valley	contiguous w/CA IBA; Greater Sage-Grouse
Gold Butte/Whitney's Pocket	Bendire's Thrasher.
Diamond Valley, lake and playa	Snowy Plover nesting colonies, wintering raptor populations
Yelland Lake Playa	Snowy Plover nesting colony
Newark Lake	Snowy Plover, Long-billed Curlew
Walker River (Mason Valley to Weber Dam)	Much of this corridor appears to be full of enticing habitat for birds. It remains largely an unknown landscape.

Kirch Wildlife Management Area

The Kirch WMA lies in the White River Valley. The site has several impounded lakes surrounded by emergent marsh vegetation, and the entire area is situated in a sea of sagebrush and grasses. Kirch is a great destination for bird watching, fishing, and camping, but the data available on bird use of the site did not meet any threshold for IBA status, and therefore the area was not nominated. Waterfowl surveys conducted January 1999-2004 revealed an average of 1,331 wintering birds, but the minimum threshold for significant congregations of wintering waterfowl is 2,000 birds. Few data were available describing passerine use of the area, which could warrant reevaluating it for IBA status, as would an increase in waterfowl use of the site.

East Fork of the Walker River

The East Fork of the Walker River has a narrow but largely healthy riparian corridor. Although there is probably not a large population of breeding birds, the river may offer important habitat for migrating songbirds. Two brief forays to the river in April and September documented limited migration, but this type of phenomenon is episodic and easy to miss. While absence of evidence does not mean evidence of absence, clearly more study is needed to assess this site. A short stretch of the river near the Nevada-California border is included in the Wellington - Pine Grove Hills IBA.

Humboldt Wildlife Management Area

The Humboldt WMA occupies portions of the Humboldt Sink, the terminous of the Humboldt River. Historically, the river reached this point, supporting a marsh complex and probably a population of waterbirds and songbirds. In the midst of a severe drought and with high upstream demands on the water, the site holds water rarely and unpredictably. The site held water in 1995 and again in 2005. In 1995 1,100 pairs of nesting White-faced Ibis were documented. Data collected intermittently in previous years also shows intriguing bird use, for example, 10,000 Long-billed Dowitchers in August of 1988. If water rights could be secured for the WMA or when the sink again holds water from natural runoff, it would be worthwhile considering this site as an IBA.

Snow-capped Mount Charleston in the Spring Mountains IBA

Appendix II – Nevada IBA Program Nomination Materials

Site Nomination Criteria

Definitions

An Important Bird Area (IBA) is a site providing essential habitat to one or more species of breeding or non-breeding birds. Sites are usually discrete and distinguishable in character, habitat, or ornithological importance from surrounding areas. Boundaries may be natural, such as watersheds, or man-made, such as roads and property boundaries. Ideally, an IBA should exist as an actual or potential protected area, or it should have the potential to be managed for the benefit of birds and other wildlife. There is no pre-determined size for an IBA, but wherever possible an IBA should be large enough to encompass the resources that are significant to the birds throughout the season for which they are important. Not all IBAs can or will meet this last definition--bottlenecks or migration corridors for raptors being one example.

Criteria

A site meeting any one of the criteria in the following five categories may qualify as an IBA. Many sites will meet several criteria. These criteria should not be considered absolute, and other factors, such as relative importance to other sites, may be weighed in making final site selections.

Category NV-1: Sites important to species of concern in Nevada.

1(a) Sites that regularly support significant breeding or non-breeding densities of one or more of the species listed as Endangered or Threatened in the state of Nevada. Applies primarily to breeding or wintering sites, though regular migratory areas may be considered if known to be of exceptional importance.

1(b) Sites that regularly support significant breeding or non-breeding densities of species identified as high conservation priorities by Partners in Flight in the Nevada Partners in Flight Bird Conservation Plan (1999).

Sites meeting criteria 1(a) or 1(b) should be those where the species occurs or potentially occurs with some regularity, not areas of infrequent occurrence. Ideally, these sites will benefit many species. The species covered by criteria 1(a) and 1(b) are listed below.

Federally Endangered Species

Brown Pelican

Wood Stork

Yuma Clapper Rail

Least Tern

Southwestern Willow Flycatcher

Federally Threatened Species

Bald Eagle

Mountain Plover (proposed)

Partners in Flight Nevada Priority List

Clark's Grebe

American White Pelican

White-faced Ibis

Cooper's Hawk

Northern Goshawk

Swainson's Hawk

Ferruginous Hawk

Prairie Falcon

Greater Sandhill Crane

Greater Sage-Grouse

Snowy Plover

American Avocet

Long-billed Curlew

Black Tern

Western Yellow-billed Cuckoo

Flammulated Owl

Burrowing Owl

Short-eared Owl

Calliope Hummingbird
Lewis's Woodpecker
Red-naped Sapsucker
White-headed Woodpecker
Three-toed Woodpecker
Olive-sided Flycatcher
Southwestern Willow Flycatcher
  (*Empidonax traillii eximus*)
Willow Flycatcher (*E. t. brewsteri, E. t.
  adastus*)
Gray Flycatcher
Ash-throated Flycatcher
Loggerhead Shrike
Gray Vireo
Pinyon Jay
Bank Swallow
Juniper Titmouse
Western Bluebird

Sage Thrasher
LeConte's Thrasher
Phainopepla
Orange-crowned Warbler
Virginia's Warbler
Lucy's Warbler
Black-throated Gray Warbler
Grace's Warbler
MacGillivray's Warbler
Wilson's Warbler
Yellow-breasted Chat
Vesper Sparrow
Sage Sparrow
Blue Grosbeak
Bobolink
Scott's Oriole
Black Rosy-Finch

Category NV-2: A site harboring an assemblage of species restricted to a unique or threatened natural community type.

The site contains an assemblage of species characteristic of a habitat type that is
2(a) rare, threatened, or unusual within the state or region;
2(b) an exceptional representative of a natural or near-natural habitat within the state or region.

This category is intended to cover relatively large areas capable of supporting significant bird populations, especially of species with particular habitat requirements such as wetland dependent or grassland nesting birds (for example, Snowy Plover, Bobolink). Small remnants of an exceptional habitat type may be included, however. Selection of sites will be based on avian assemblages with the habitat community type, not on the habitat community type alone. Characteristic species of birds and other wildlife indicative of the habitat type should be identified and, if possible, quantified.

Category NV-3: Sites where significant numbers of birds concentrate for breeding, migration, or over-wintering.

Sites that regularly hold significant numbers of one or more species, breeding or non-breeding, including migration, and including sites supporting a high diversity of bird species. Significant numbers are subjectively defined, but should include 1 percent or more of the state's population. The guidelines indicated below provide some logical thresholds for site selection. Except where indicated, numerical estimates should be based on a short period of time, such as one-time counts on daily surveys, not on cumulative totals. Introduced, naturalized, and nuisance birds (e.g., Starlings, Canada Geese) will not be used to designate a site.

3(a) Congregations of waterfowl: The site regularly supports at least 2,000 breeding/wintering waterfowl or 5,000 migrating waterfowl. "Waterfowl" includes such birds as loons, grebes, ducks, coots, and moorhens.

3(b) Congregations of gulls or terns: The site regularly supports at least 1,000 gulls or 50 terns over a short period of time during any season.

3(c) Congregations of shorebirds: The site regularly supports 1,000 or more shorebirds at one time.

3(d) Congregations of raptors: The site is a migratory corridor for at least 1,000 raptors (seasonal total) during spring or fall migration, or is a winter concentration area used by at least 100 raptors. The area may include topographic features that funnel birds through a particular site.

3(e) Concentrations of wading birds: The site regularly supports 100 or more pairs of wading birds (herons, egrets, ibises, stilts, avocets).

3(f) Congregations of migratory land birds: The site is an important migratory stopover, bottleneck, or migratory corridor. Sites should contain exceptional numbers and/or diversity. No absolute threshold in numbers is set.

3(g) Single species concentrations: The site regularly supports significant concentrations of a congregatory species but may not meet the thresholds for specific groups of birds listed in criteria 3a-3f above. Such sites should support a higher proportion of a species counted on a statewide basis than other comparable areas.

Supplementary Criteria

The following two criteria may be used to supplement or support a site nomination. By themselves, they are insufficient to warrant the designation of a site in Nevada as an IBA. In addition to the two criteria described below, you are encouraged to list other outstanding resources that characterize the site you are nominating (see nomination form).

Category NV-4: Sites supporting long-term avian research efforts.

Sites protected under this criterion should be a natural area where a long-term avian research project is based. Past or ongoing research at the site should have contributed substantially to ornithology, avian ecology, or bird conservation. Publication of relevant findings in a widely recognized, peer-reviewed journal (e.g., The Auk, Condor, Wilson Bulletin, American Birds, Journal of Field Ornithology, Ecology, Conservation Biology) is one of the primary considerations. Breeding Bird Survey blocks and Christmas Bird Count routes, while important within the context of their own programs, will not qualify an area as an IBA.

Category NV-5: Sites providing important, bird-specific educational opportunities.

Sites supporting educational programs in which a significant component of the program content focuses on avian ecology, bird identification, biodiversity, or the value of high-quality habitat for birds. Sites may be in a natural, urban, suburban, or rural setting, but should retain significant natural habitat. Sites where educational programs are being developed will also be considered, as will sites where habitat restoration is a significant management goal.

Further Information

If you require further assistance or need to obtain the nomination form that should accompany these criteria, please contact the IBA Program at the address below. You may also wish to check the web at www.NevadaAudubon.org for information and assistance.

SITE NOMINATION FORM

The Nevada IBA Program is conducting an inventory of habitats that may qualify as Important Bird Areas. To qualify, a site needs to meet only *one* of the IBA criteria, although many sites will meet several. Using the accompanying guidelines, please tell us about areas that you think may meet the criteria. Complete as much of this form as possible. It is recommended that you contact the IBA coordinator *before* completing this form. The coordinator can inform you if the site has already been nominated, and may also be able to provide you with data or contacts to support your nomination. Up-to-date program information can also be found at www.NevadaAudubon.org. Thank you!

General Information

SITE NAME_____   Approximate size (acres)_____

Nearest Town(s)_____ County_____

Latitude _____°_____' Longitude _____°_____' or UTM _____N _____E

(Zone 11 NAD 27 Projection)

Approx. elevation (in feet); if a range, give low-high _____

General description of the site (habitat, location, prominent features, ownership, and any other helpful information):

IBA Criteria (check *all* that apply): PLEASE READ ACCOMPANYING DETAILED CRITERIA FOR SITE SELECTION BEFORE COMPLETING THIS SECTION

☐ Criterion NV-1(a): Regularly supports significant densities of one or more of the species listed as Endangered or Threatened in the state of Nevada. (Explain below).

☐ Criterion NV-1(b): Regularly supports significant densities of species identified as high conservation priorities in the Nevada Partners in Flight Bird Conservation Plan (1999). (Explain below).

☐ Criterion NV-2(a): Harbors an assemblage of species characteristic of a habitat type that is rare, threatened, or unusual within the state or region. (Explain below).

☐ Criterion NV-2(b): Harbors an assemblage of species characteristic of a habitat type that is an exceptional representative of a natural or near-natural habitat within the state or region. (Explain below).

☐ Criterion NV-3(a): Sites with significant numbers of waterfowl. (Explain below).

☐ Criterion NV-3(b): Sites with significant numbers of gulls or terns. (Explain below).

☐ Criterion NV-3(c): Sites with significant numbers of shorebirds. (Explain below).

☐ Criterion NV-3(d): Sites with significant numbers of raptors. (Explain below).

☐ Criterion NV-3(e): Sites with significant numbers of wading birds. (Explain below).

☐ Criterion NV-3(f): Sites with significant numbers of migratory land birds. (Explain below).

☐ Criterion NV-3(g): Sites with significant numbers of single species concentrations. (Explain below).

Supplementary criteria:

☐ Criterion NV-4: Sites supporting long-term avian research efforts. (Explain below).

☐ Category NV-5: Sites providing important, bird-specific educational opportunities. (Explain below).

Why is this site important for Nevada birds? (Provide additional details):

Other Resources: Please describe any significant flora and non-avian fauna, social, cultural, economic, or historic uses associated with this site:

Ornithological Importance

List the species for which this site is important, the season(s) for which the site is important, average or maximum numbers (estimates are okay), the years on which this count or estimate is based, and sources of information.

Species	Season[1]	Avg. #/Season	Max. #/Season	Which Years?	Sources[2]

Species	Season[1]	Avg. #/Season	Max. #/Season	Which Years?	Sources[2]

[1] (On which quantitative data are based): B=Breeding, W=Winter, SM=Spring Migration, FM=Fall Migration

[2] Sources: 1=published reports, 2=surveys (Christmas Bird Count, Breeding Bird Survey, etc), 3=personal observation

Specify Sources:

Habitat and land use

___Salt Desert Scrub

___Sagebrush

___Pinyon-Juniper

___Mojave Shrub

___Mesquite/Catclaw

___Lowland Riparian

___Montane Shrub

___Mountain Mahogany

___Montane Riparian

___Montane Parkland

___Wetlands and Lakes

___Coniferous Forest

___Cliffs and Talus

___Aspen

___Agricultural Lands

___Other (specify)

Major Land Uses: Please estimate the % of time that the proposed site is used for the following purposes:

___Nature and Wildlife Conservation

___Hunting/Fishing

___Other Recreation or Tourism

___Agriculture/Livestock

___Forestry

___Water Supply

___Utility/Right-of-way

___Suburban/Residential

___Urban/Commercial

___Research

___Undeveloped

___Other(specify)

Land Ownership/Management (Check all that apply):

☐ State ☐ Federal ☐ Municipal ☐ Private   ☐ Tribal

Conservation and Other Resources

Primary Conservation Issues: Please note threats to the site as Serious (S), Minor (M), or Potential (P).

_____ Invasive or Non-native Plants

_____ Introduced Animals

_____ Cowbird Parasitism

_____ Predators

_____ Pollution

_____ Habitat Conversion

_____ Development

_____ Disturbance to Birds or Habitat

_____ Hydrologic Changes

_____ Off Road Vehicle Use

_____ Other (describe)

Describe primary conservation issues, their seriousness, and any steps being taken to address them:

Is habitat restoration or enhancement of this site needed? Yes or No.

If the site does need restoration or enhancement, what actions need to be taken (e.g., fencing, planting, stream bank stabilization, erosion checks, exotic species management, etc.)?

Local groups with an interest in this site:

Name/Group_____   Zip_____
Address_____   Phone_____
City _____ State _____

Land Owner/Manager Contacts: Please provide the name, address, and phone numbers of the landowner or land manager(s) for the site, and indicate whether they have been contacted and/or given permission for the site to be nominated.

Name/Group_____   Name/Group_____
Address_____   Address_____
City State   City State
Zip_____   Zip_____
Phone_____   Phone_____
Contacted?   Contacted?
Permission?_____   Permission?_____

Your Name_____ Phone _____
Address _____ Fax _____
City_____ State _____ Zip _____ email _____
Audubon Chapter or Other Affiliation _____

Supporting documentation is required (Topographic maps, photos, field notes, checklists, etc.) attach supporting materials and return to Nevada Important Bird Areas Program. You may e-mail this form if you are filling it out online and send your maps and supporting material by snail mail or as an attachment. On behalf of the birds, thank you!

READ AND MAKE SURE YOU UNDERSTAND THE GUIDELINES AND CRITERIA. Please submit one form for each site that you think matches one or more of the criteria.

OBTAIN A MAP OF THE AREA WHERE YOUR SITE IS LOCATED. Send the map indicating your site (including approximate boundaries) along with the rest of the nomination materials. Keep a copy of the map for your records. A USGS Topographic map (7.5' series, 1:24 000 scale) is preferred. These can be ordered by calling 1-800-USA-MAPS or on the web at www.usgs.gov. They may also be available locally, depending on where you live.

GENERAL INFORMATION

Site Name: Use the most common name by which the site is known. For larger sites, use the name of the largest single unit within the area, or most easily recognized name, such as a national forest, lake, or other geographic feature.

Approx. size (in acres): For many public sites (parks, refuges) this information is available from the land manager.

Nearest town/County: Write the name of the town nearest to the site, and county where the site is located.

Latitude/Longitude or UTMs: Select the approximate center of the site and determine its lat/long or UTM location.

Approximate elevation: Estimated from topo maps and written in feet. If the site has a wide range of elevations (for example a steeply sloped area), give the approximate range of elevations at the site (example, "4,000-5,500 feet").

Criteria: VERY IMPORTANT. Check the box or boxes for the criteria that you think your site meets. In the space following each criterion, describe briefly why this site is important and for which species or groups of birds the site is important. Example: "This is an exceptional migratory corridor for raptors with an average of 6,000 birds of 8 species each fall."

Your information: We may need to contact you for additional information and with updates.

ORNITHOLOGICAL IMPORTANCE

Species (or Group) Name: Write the full name of each species (e.g., Juniper Titmouse) or group (e.g., Herons) for which this site is important. The species or groups listed should correspond to the criteria checked. For example, if you checked Category 1(a) and indicated Bald Eagle, then you should list Bald Eagle in the table. If you checked 3(c) for shorebirds, try to give total numbers for individual species, if you know them.

Season: Indicate the season or seasons for which this site is important for this particular species. Feel free to use more than one line to indicate breeding season and migration totals (for example) if the species occurs on the site in more than one season.

Avg. Numbers/Season: Write in the best available estimate for the average number of individuals (or pairs) using the site during the season for which it is important. For example, for a raptor species under Criterion 3(d), you would write "2,750/season." For a species of waterfowl in winter, "8,000/day."

Max. Numbers/Season: Write in the best available estimate for the average number of individuals (or pairs) using the site during the season for which it is important, over a given period of time, in the format indicated above.

Which Years?: Write in the approximate years on which your numerical estimates are based (e.g., 1996-2000).

Sources: Indicate the code number that best describes where your data for this species come from. Specify any published or documented sources in the space below the table.

HABITAT AND LAND-USE. Fill in the information as indicated on the form. Include a description of the most significant conservation issues facing bird populations or the habitat at the site. Provide as much detailed information as you can. This information will be essential to help guide future conservation efforts for the site. Include a description of any conservation measures known for the site. Include information on whether the site is protected as a park or other type of conservation area, or has any other conservation designations (e.g., conservation easement, Western Hemisphere Shorebird Reserve Network, etc.). Include information on any conservation or management plans that exist for the site or that are currently being developed, as well as any noteworthy suggestions that have been made for conserving the site.

IF YOU ARE HAVING DIFFICULTY, CONTACT THE IBA COORDINATOR. The form should be as complete as possible, but does not have to be 100% complete to submit it. Do the best you can. We can help if you need more information.

Appendix III – Global and Continental Thresholds for U.S. IBAs

Table 1. Global (A1) IBA thresholds for species with significant populations in Nevada.

Common Name	Threatened Species Code +	Breeding (pairs/individual) threshold	Migration (individuals) threshold	Non-br (individuals) threshold	Audubon WatchList - Red or Yellow	USFWS Birds of Cons. Concern	Global pop. estimate	Global Population Trend *
Greater Sage-Grouse	N	40/120	60	60	Y		150k	ld
Ferruginous Hawk	N	10/30	30	30	Y	x	23k (5.8K-14K)	i
Long-billed Curlew	N	10/30	60	60	R	x	20,000	d
Spotted Owl	N	10/30	30	30	R		15,000	d
Olive-sided Flycatcher	N	30/90	90	x	Y	x	1,200k	ld
Bell's Vireo	N	30/90	90	x	R	x	1,500k	ld
Pinyon Jay	V	30/90	90	90	Y		4,100k	ld
Bendire's Thrasher	V	10/30	30	30	R	x	170k	ld
Brewer's Sparrow	N	40/120	120	120	Y	x	16,000k	ld
Cassin's Finch	N	60/180	180	180			1,900k	d

+ Threatened species: V=vulnerable, N=near-threatened

* Global population trend: d=declining, ld=large decline, i=increasing

Table 2. Continental (B1) IBA thresholds for species with significant populations in Nevada.

Common Name	Audubon WatchList - Red/Yellow	Federally Listed Species	USFWS Birds Cons. Conc.	PIF population size score	Breeding threshold - (pairs/individuals)	Migration threshold	Winter threshold	Global pop estimate	Global Population Trend *	N. American pop estimate	N. Am. Population Trend
Trumpeter Swan	Y			5	20/60	240	240			23,647	i
Blue Grouse	Y			3	60/180	180	180	2,600k	ld		
Mountain Quail	Y			4	40/120	480	480	160k	?		
Bald Eagle		T		4	20/60	240	240	330K	i	330k	l
Northern Harrier			x	3	60/180	180	180	1,300K	d	455k	4
Swainson's Hawk	Y		x	4	40/120	480	480	490K	?	490k	3
Peregrine Falcon			x	3	60/180	180	180	1,200K	i	?	l
Snowy Plover	R	(T)		4	20/60	60	240			17.4-18K	d,d,d
Marbled Godwit	Y		x	4	40/120	480	480			171,500	d,d,x
Wilson's Phalarope	Y		x	3	60/180	720	720			1,500k	d
Band-tailed Pigeon	Y			3	60/180	720	720	3,900k	ld		
Western Yellow-billed Cuckoo			x	?(2)	20/60	60	x				
Flammulated Owl	Y		x	5	20/60	60	60	37k	?		
Burrowing Owl			x	3	60/180	180	180	2,000k	d		
Short-eared Owl	Y		x	3	60/180	180	180	2,400k	ld		
White-throated Swift	Y			4	160/480	480	480	410k	ld		
Costa's Hummingbird	Y			3	60/180	180	180	3,600k	?		
Calliope Hummingbird	Y			3	60/180	180	x	1,000k	?		
Rufous Hummingbird	Y		x	2	80/240	240	x	6,500k	ld		
Lewis's Woodpecker	Y		x	4	40/120	120	120	130k	?		
Williamson's Sapsucker			x	4	40/120	120	120	310k	?		
Red-naped Sapsucker			x	3	60/180	180	180	2,200k	?		
White-headed Woodpecker	Y		x	4	40/120	120	120	72k	s		
Gilded Flicker	Y			3	60/180	180	180	1,100k	s		
Southwest Willow Flycatcher	Y	E		?(3)	20/60	60	60				
Willow Flycatcher (except *extimus*)	Y			3	120/360	360	360	3,300k	d		
Loggerhead Shrike (except mearnsi)			x	3	120/360	360	360	4,200k	ld		
Gray Vireo	Y		x	4	80/240	240	240	410k	s		
Crissal Thrasher			x	4	80/240	240	240	260k	s		
Le Conte's Thrasher	Y		x	4	80/240	240	240	190k	?		
Virginia's Warbler	Y			4	80/240	240	x	410k	?		
Lucy's Warbler	Y			3	120/360	360	x	1,200k	?		
Grace's Warbler	Y		x	3	120/360	360	x	2,000k	d		
Black-chinned Sparrow	Y		x	4	80/240	240	240	390k	d		
Tricolored Blackbird	Y		x	4	160/480	480	480	250k	ld		
Black Rosy-Finch	Y			5	40/120	240	240	20k	?		

+ Threatened species: E = Endangered, T = Threatened

* Global population trend: d = declining, ld = large decline, s = stable, l = increasing, ? = unknown

References: Morrison et al. (2001), Kushlan et al. (2002), Wetlands International (2002), BirdLife International (2004b), Rich et al. (2004).

Appendix IV – Important *Birding* Areas? Birding Nevada's IBAs

The Important Bird Areas Program is predicated on conservation, first and foremost. That said, there is certainly a link between bird watching and conservation. The IBA Program is working to cultivate a community of avid birders and develop them into citizen-scientists who will participate in monitoring IBAs, as well as working on restoration and enhancement efforts at these sites. The step from birder to citizen-scientist is actually a very small one, and a lot of people who consider themselves birders may be surprised to find they have already crossed the line and are in fact citizen-scientists.

The term citizen-scientist may have been coined by Thomas Jefferson, who used it in reference to Lewis and Clark. Jefferson himself embodied the ideal and dabbled in many disciplines throughout his life and made significant contributions in more than a few areas. But the connection with Lewis and Clark is strong, and what better heritage to celebrate in the bicentennial of the famous explorers' journey?

Becoming a citizen-scientist in the context of the IBA Program means following a set of simple guidelines that will ensure bird numbers at IBAs will be counted in a structured and repeatable fashion. At its core the undertaking still entails what we all like to do–go bird watching. But in order for the day's outing to contribute to the IBA Program, we need birders to visit the same area of an IBA so that trends in bird numbers can be tracked over the years. We also need numbers of birds seen to be recorded. A simple species list without total numbers is interesting but will in the long run tell us far less about the bird community than if we know *how many* of *which species* are seen at an IBA. Finally, we need to get the information in hand here at the IBA Program, either through a direct submission to our office or through the Nevada Birds List Server, which is both archived and searchable. The point, though, is that this need will entail bird watching on IBAs, which leads us to the topic at hand.

Visiting Nevada's IBAs for the purpose of bird watching is almost always possible, but a number of factors need to be taken into consideration. First and foremost is that visitors should keep in mind that some of Nevada's IBAs contain private lands and, in the case of the Boyd Humboldt Valley Wetlands IBA, the IBA is entirely in private ownership. Because private land lies within an IBA does not grant permission for visitation to the private land portion of the IBA. Land owner permission to visit these areas is a requirement prior to visiting.

Another issue to consider when pondering a visit to IBAs is that they are landscapes recognized as critical to the conservation of birds, and in many cases these sites are recognized because they offer important breeding habitat. That means that during spring and summer breeding season some or all of an IBA could be sensitive to human intrusion. The result of visiting at this sensitive time of year could be a lot of distraught birds, failed clutches and abandoned nests, and a landscape of significantly lower value to the birds. Fortunately, all of the IBAs with public land do have places to visit year-round, and the bird watching experience is often as good or better than that lying within sensitive areas.

A final point to keep in mind is that many of Nevada's IBAs are in remote areas with difficult access. These landscapes were chosen because of their value to birds, not birders. Access was not a factor in their selection.

With all these caveats in mind, those IBAs where visitation is appropriate and feasible include a brief description to facilitate access (Visiting the Site). There are other sources of information which the traveler may decide make a better travel guide. Chief among those is the Nevada Birding Map (Lahontan Audubon Society 2004). Another suggested travel companion is *A Birding Guide to Reno and Beyond* (Lahontan Audubon Society 2000).

Every birder, whether bagging IBAs or simply going for a stroll in a city park, should adhere to the American Birding Association's (ABA) Code of Birding Ethics. ABA's guidelines assure birding remains a valued pastime that is welcomed by communities and land owners and that avoids devaluing the very resource that attracted us to the avocation in the first place. The ABA Birding Code of Ethics is available from www.americanbirding.org/abaethics.htm.

The bird watchers' salute; Spring Wings Festival, 2005

Don McIvor is the Nevada Director of Bird Conservation, a joint position between the Lahontan Audubon Society and the National Audubon Society. Don holds a BA in Environmental Sciences from the University of Virginia and an MS in Wildlife Ecology from Utah State University. His previous publications include *Birding Utah* (Falcon Press), peer-reviewed papers in the scientific literature, and numerous articles and photographs in popular publications. Don is a former managing editor at *Petroglyph*, and contributing editor at *Edging West*. When not at work, Don can be found turning wood, playing music, or wielding his camera in the remotest place he can find.